Three Murders, a Suicide and a Near Miss

INTERMEDIATE

Alison Chaplin

AUTHOR
Alison Chaplin

EDITOR
Joel Lane

ASSISTANT EDITOR
Roanne Davis

SERIES DESIGNER
Anna Oliwa/Heather Sanneh

DESIGNER
Anna Oliwa

ILLUSTRATIONS
Wendy Lander

COVER ARTWORK
Charlotte Combe

Text © 2000 Alison Chaplin
© 2000 Scholastic Ltd

Designed using Adobe Pagemaker

Published by Scholastic Ltd,
Villiers House,
Clarendon Avenue,
Leamington Spa,
Warwickshire CV32 5PR

1 2 3 4 5 6 7 8 9 0   0 1 2 3 4 5 6 7 8 9

British Library Cataloguing-in-Publication Data. A catalogue record for this book is available from the British Library.

ISBN 0-439-01749-1

ACKNOWLEDGEMENTS

First performed in Manchester by participants on the 'Drama and Theatre Workshop' in August 1996, and again in October 1999. Many thanks to all the children for their suggestions of script changes and enthusiastic performances!

For permission to give a performance of this play at which an admission charge is made, please contact the Editorial Department, Educational Books, Scholastic Limited, Villiers House, Clarendon Avenue, Leamington Spa, Warks., CV32 5PR. You do not need to seek permission if you do not charge an entry fee for the performance. Performing licences must be applied for prior to beginning rehearsals.

Fees are £10.00 per performance for a paying audience of up to 200 people and £15.00 per performance for paying audiences of 200 people or over.

Alison Chaplin is the drama consultant for the Borough of Stockport and manager of 'Arts on the Move', a company specializing in providing a range of drama and theatre services. For information call 0161 881 0868.

CONTENTS LIST

Three Murders,
a Suicide and
a Near Miss

INTRODUCTION

USING THIS BOOK

The aim of this Scholastic Performance Play is to provide teachers with the appropriate resources to read, rehearse and perform a short play. The book enables teachers and children to understand the process of interpreting scripts and the approaches needed for successful rehearsals and performances. From providing pre-rehearsal support to supplying linked reading and writing tasks, the book is structured in a way that assumes no prior knowledge of script work and no previous experience of staging performances, leading all those involved through the process in easy-to-follow stages.

WORKSHOP SESSIONS

Workshop sessions are provided to help the teacher introduce the children to the concept of drama. The sessions help the children to:

- read and understand playscripts
- explore the implicit themes and issues within the play
- appreciate character development
- learn the skills required for performance.

Each session is structured to approach a different aspect of working with a playscript, using methods which are both practical and enjoyable.

PLAYSCRIPT

The playscript is organized in an easy-to-follow format, complete with full stage directions and scene changes. At the beginning of each script, following the cast list, there is a set of brief character outlines that provide an indication of behavioural traits and help the children to understand how each role should be performed. Most of the plays in the *Performance Plays* series are simple to stage and require little in the way of make-up, costume or setting.

PRODUCTION SUPPORT

The production support notes provide practical advice to support the teacher through the various stages from the beginning to the end of the production process, including: holding auditions; structuring rehearsals; simple and effective staging, props, costumes and make-up; and finally, presenting a professional 'curtain call' after the performance.

The ideas provided have arisen from the author's own experience of directing this play, and are thus informed by a knowledge of what has worked in practice. However, they are not meant to be completely prescriptive: if teachers feel that they have the resources, time and skills to create more elaborate staging and costumes, or to approach the performance in a different way, then they should feel free to do so!

LITERACY SUPPORT

The literacy support notes at the end of this book are directly linked to the requirements of the National Literacy Strategy *Framework for Teaching*. They provide suggestions for supportive tasks, organized under the headings: 'Story', 'Characters', 'Theme', 'Working with playscript layout' and 'Performance-related tasks'. Again, these are not completely prescriptive; but they provide teachers with examples of how the playscript can be used to generate structured literacy work.

A FLEXIBLE RESOURCE

The unique aspect of these Performance Plays is that their contents can be utilized in a number of different ways: as a simple reading resource; to provide a basis for literacy tasks; to introduce children to the concept of performance drama; or to produce a full-scale school play. Readers should feel free to employ the book in any way that meets their needs. However, the most important approach for anyone using this play is to be flexible, enthusiastic and prepared to 'have a go'!

GUIDANCE FOR WORKING WITH SCRIPTS

If the children have no previous experience of script work, it is a good idea to lead them through the following simple drama process in order to make them familiar with the concept and style of a scripted performance.

Ask the children (in their classroom places) to find a partner and hold a conversation with him or her. It could be about anything: the television programmes they watched the night before, their favourite books, what they did during the school holidays, and so on. Allow these conversations to run for about a minute, then ask the children to stop talking.

Now ask the pairs to label themselves 'A' and 'B'. Tell them that they must hold a conversation again, but this time 'B' cannot respond until 'A' has finished talking (or until 'A' has finished a sentence, if 'A' is going on for too long). Insist that the children adhere to this procedure for speaking and responding, as this forms the basis for most scripted formats.

Allow these structured conversations to run for about a minute, then ask the children to stop talking. Invite them to give feedback on the type of conversations they had. Using the board, write their statements and responses in the form of an 'A said' and 'B said' structure:

A said: ....

B said: ....

Record just a couple of lines from each conversation, to show the children how these conversations can be recorded. Ask them to suggest how their second conversation was different from their first one. Answers should include: the speakers had names (as in 'A' and 'B'); they could only speak when the other person had finished speaking; the conversations were not as natural; they had to listen more carefully and think more about what they said and how they responded to their partners.

Now ask the children to join with another pair to make a four. (Odd numbers or unequal groups are also acceptable.) Ask them to hold an initial unstructured conversation with each other on a subject of your choosing; leave these to run for about a minute. Then ask the children to label themselves 'A', 'B', 'C' and 'D' (if there are four in the group) and to hold another conversation, this time following the same restriction as before: while someone in the group is talking, no-one else can speak. Tell the children that they do not necessarily have to join in the conversation in alphabetical order.

Invite feedback about these conversations. Again, ask for comments on how the second discussion differed from the first. Record part of a structured conversation on the board, using 'A', 'B', 'C' and 'D' to indicate who speaks which lines.

Inform the children that this is how plays are structured: they are written records of people speaking to each other, having conversations or discussions; that the name of the character speaking is indicated at the beginning of each piece of dialogue.

Further practice for the children could include:

● recording their conversations in script form, using the 'A' and 'B' or 'A', 'B', 'C', 'D' format.
● devising and writing original conversations, using the 'A' and 'B' or 'A', 'B', 'C', 'D' format.
● lifting a section of dialogue from a familiar story and rewriting it in script form.
● rewriting their own conversations, using names instead of letters of the alphabet.
● improvising a scene (such as someone buying an item in a shop), recording it using a tape recorder or Dictaphone, then replaying the recording in order to write it down as a script.

The main aim is to help the children appreciate that a playscript is simply dialogue, conversations or verbal statements written down, and that the format gives a clear indication of who is speaking at any one time.

Advise the children that characters may interrupt each other, but that two people will never talk at the same time during a scripted performance: the lines will always be spoken in sequence. Make sure they understand that playscripts (unlike other forms of written speech) do not contain speech marks or quotation marks, because the whole text is known and understood to be speech and so they are unnecessary.

Go on from this exercise to reading and discussing an extract from any playscript: explore how the text indicates who is speaking, analyse the sequencing of the dialogue and reaffirm the idea of characters speaking in turn.

As a final note, when reading the playscript in this book, ask the children to suggest what the purpose of the words in brackets and italics may be. They may reply: 'How characters say things', 'What characters do' or 'How characters do things'. Keep the language as simple as this initially, developing their vocabulary gradually as they become more familiar with reading and understanding scripts. (See 'Literacy support' on page 56.)

THEMES AND ISSUES IN THE PLAY

Three Murders, A Suicide and a Near Miss is based on Shakespeare's *Othello,* with the original text simplified and translated into modern language. The complete story of Othello has been 'edited' for its essential highlights, but enough remains for readers to appreciate the dramatic context.

The themes of Shakespeare's original text remain also. The play is centred on the jealousy felt by both Iago and Othello. The former is due to Iago's arrogance, the latter to Othello's insecurities. However, in both cases, this jealousy leads to revenge – with dramatic and tragic consequences.

Othello is portrayed in this version as a somewhat ignorant and bumbling man, though he is far more noble in the original version. However, I felt that his willingness to believe in the infidelity of his wife and his resulting drastic actions made him deserving of some criticism. Iago is the archetypal villain, and should be played with as much venom as possible. The juxtaposition of these two characters could lead to discussions concerning the concepts of 'good' and 'evil'; however, children may find it difficult to associate Othello's actions with the word 'good'. He is by no means the 'hero' of the story.

The play allows children access to one of Shakespeare's great stories, without the constraints of having to understand Elizabethan language. However, *Three Murders, A Suicide and a Near Miss* can provide a focus for comparisons between this play and short sections of the original text. It can also provide work for history lessons, giving children opportunities to explore social and personal issues from Elizabethan times – and, in particular, from the time of Shakespeare's life.

The style of the play, with its announcer, villain and heroine, is based loosely on the elements contained in Victorian melodramas. This aspect of the performance and presentation style could easily be emphasized. This approach could encourage additional investigation into Victorian theatre or music-hall, and the play could be further adapted to meet these criteria more precisely.

On a simpler level, the children will enjoy discussing the characters, their actions, motives and reactions, and the idea of the tragedy that hangs over and then falls upon them.

WORKSHOP SESSIONS

These sessions should take place before any rehearsal or practical application of the playscript. They introduce the children to drama and theatre, develop their speaking and listening skills, generate positive group interaction, increase their level of concentration, help to prepare them for the types of activity they will be doing during work on the playscript, and develop their ability to perform confidently and effectively.

SESSION 1:
INTRODUCTORY WARM-UP

Timing: Spend no more than 15 minutes on each individual activity. The whole session should take no more than 45 minutes.

Resources: A large space (such as the school hall), chairs or cushions (one per child), a large piece of fabric or a piece of chalk, cloth to rub out chalk marks (if used).

Objectives: To introduce the children to the concept of drama, promote positive group interaction and encourage the children to respond appropriately to instructions.

TOUCH AND FREEZE!
DEVELOPS CONCENTRATION, LISTENING SKILLS AND GROUP INTERACTION

Ask two volunteers to sit cross-legged on the floor, with their hands resting in their laps. Ask the other children to place one finger gently anywhere on the bodies of those seated. The sitting children will need to be reasonably upright, so that the others do not fall over them.

Explain that when you shout 'Touch and freeze!', the children sitting down should swing their arms around, trying to touch those who are standing with their fingers placed on them. At the same time, the standing children should try to avoid the swinging arms. The 'sitting' children cannot move from their sitting position when trying to touch the others and the 'touching' children must continue to touch the sitting child. Anyone who breaks these rules will be disqualified!

When all of the standing children have placed their fingers on those seated, allow a dramatic pause before calling out 'Touch and freeze!' This pause creates tension, instils silence and builds concentration. When the command 'Touch and freeze!' has been responded to, any children who have been touched by those seated should join them on the floor.

Repeat the exercise several times, instructing the children to place 'fingers on', calling out 'Touch and freeze!' and asking those touched to join the others sitting on the ground. Continue until you have a winner.

Play two or three times. Then ask the children to sit in a circle, and go on to...

WINK MURDER
CREATES TENSION AND INTRODUCES PERFORMANCE SKILLS

With the children in a circle on the floor, or on chairs. Choose one child to be the 'detective'. Ask this child either to leave the room or to turn away from the circle. Ask the remaining children to close their eyes and bow their heads – they must not look!

Walk around the outside of the circle and tap one of the children on the back. This child has now become the 'murderer'. Do not reveal the identity of the murderer to the other players. Ask the children to raise their heads and open their eyes again.

Explain that the chosen 'murderer' is going to 'murder' children sitting in the circle by winking silently at them. (Children who find it difficult to wink can blink both eyes instead.) Those children who are 'wink murdered' should 'die' horribly, noisily and dramatically! No one sitting in the circle should reveal the identity of the murderer.

As soon as the murderer has been chosen, invite the detective back and ask him or her to stand in the centre of the circle. The murderer must try to 'wink murder' people without being identified by the detective. The detective must try to guess the identity

of the murderer. Allow the detective two or three guesses, then reveal who the murderer is.

Choosing a new detective and murderer each time, play for several rounds, then move quickly on to...

RAFT
ENCOURAGES QUICK RESPONSES AND GROUP CO-OPERATION

Put away any chairs used and ask the children to stand in an open space. Spread a large piece of fabric on the floor in the centre of the room, or draw a large square with the chalk (this is a safer option on polished floors). Tell the children that this is the 'Raft'.

Explain that you are going to ask them to 'swim' around the room. When you shout 'Shark!' they all have to try and get onto the raft. Any children not managing to get on, or stay on, the raft are out and play no further part in the game. They will have to sit at the side and watch the others.

Ask the children to 'swim' around the room, discouraging them from swimming close to the raft. After a short while, call out 'Shark!' When you have eliminated those children who failed to get on to, or stay on, the raft, fold the piece of material in half or reduce the size of the chalk square.

Repeat the instructions, pointing out to the children that the raft is smaller now. After they have swum around the room and responded to your call of 'Shark!', and you have eliminated those children who didn't manage to stay on the raft, reduce the size of the raft again.

Continue until you have two or three players remaining, with a very small fabric or chalk square.

When you have found a winner (or two winners), thank the children for their efforts. Ask them to sit in a circle with you, and end with...

CIRCLE

CHILDREN REFLECT ON AND EVALUATE THEIR SKILLS

When the children are settled on the floor, cushions or chairs, ask them if they have enjoyed the drama session. Invite their opinions and reasons. What do they think they have learned and achieved?

This discussion gives an indication of any skills and knowledge gained, and can be used as a basis for developing the children's abilities during later workshop sessions.

SESSION 2:
APPROACHING THE TEXT

Timing: Spend up to 15 minutes on each activity. The whole session should take no more than 60 minutes.

Resources: Copies of the script (one per child), a board or flip chart, writing materials, a sheet of A3 paper, Blu-Tack (or similar), a marker pen.

Objective: To familiarize children with the playscript text.

SHARED TEXT WORK

WHOLE-CLASS READING OF THE SCRIPT

Sit with the children in a circle, or with them in their classroom places. Give each child a copy of the playscript, and keep one for yourself. If applicable, remind the children of their earlier drama exercise on understanding scripts (see page 5).

Tell the children that you are all going to read a play called *Three Murders, a Suicide and a Near Miss*. Say that you will read the lines spoken by some of the characters, and will ask some of them to read the lines for other characters. Ask the children to read and follow the words in the script while they are being read.

Read through the script scene by scene, combining your reading with that of volunteers or nominees. (NB Read the spoken lines spoken only: do not name each speaker in turn, and do not read the stage directions aloud.) A suggested distribution of reading parts is as follows:

● SCENE 1: Volunteers or nominees read the lines spoken by CASSIO, MESSENGER 1, MESSENGER 2 and RODERIGO. You read the lines spoken by other characters.

● SCENE 2: Volunteers or nominees read the lines spoken by GUARD 1, GUARD 3, BRABANTINO, RODERIGO and OTHELLO. You read the lines spoken by other characters.

● SCENE 3: Volunteers or nominees read the lines spoken by EMILIA and TIFFANIA. You read the lines spoken by BIANCA.

● SCENE 4: Volunteers or nominees read the lines spoken by CLOWN, MONTANO and MESSENGER 2. You read the lines spoken by other characters.

● SCENE 5: Volunteers or nominees read the lines spoken by CASSIO, RODERIGO, IAGO and DESDEMONA. You read the lines spoken by other characters.

● SCENE 6: Volunteers or nominees read the lines spoken by RODERIGO, GRATIANO and MONTANO. You read the lines spoken by other characters.

● SCENE 7: Volunteers or nominees read the lines spoken by EMILIA, IAGO, GRATIANO, MONTANO and LODOVICO. You read the lines spoken by other characters.

Select your readers carefully, making sure that they are proficient enough to read the lines allocated to them while also giving lower-ability readers an opportunity to read some of the lines.

At the end of each section of reading, and the play, thank the children for their efforts. Afterwards, ask them to turn back to the first page of their scripts, and move quickly on to...

FOCUSED WORD WORK

EXPLORING THE LANGUAGE USED IN THE PLAYSCRIPT

Invite the children to identify words from the text that they have difficulty in understanding. Specify that these must be words which they have never seen or heard before reading the play. Write these words on the board. Work through the script quickly, recording as many suggestions as possible from the children.

Use any remaining time to find definitions of as many of these words as you can. This could be achieved in a number of different ways:

● Children looking up the words in a dictionary, working individually with teacher guidance.
● Children working in pairs or small groups, being allocated three or four words per pair or group and looking them up in a dictionary.
● The teacher providing definitions of the words on the board.

● The teacher providing definitions of some of the words on the board, but asking the children to discover the definitions of others.

● The teacher encouraging the children to define words from their context in the playscript.

The process of defining words can be made more interesting by creating teams and allocating a 'team point' each time a word is defined correctly. Make sure that the children record the words, and that their definitions are recorded – on paper, in spelling books or in writing books.

Leave any words not defined for further work at a later time, and move on to...

GROUP WORK

SMALL-GROUP READINGS OF THE PLAYSCRIPT

Arrange the children in seven groups of three to six. (It is best if these are of mixed reading ability.) Make sure that each child has a copy of the playscript. Tell them that you are going to ask each group to read out a scene from the play, with different group members speaking the lines of different characters.

They will be expected to read *all* of the lines spoken by the different characters in their scenes, and that this may mean some children reading the lines for more than one character. Advise them to negotiate and distribute the character parts quickly and fairly, and to make sure that each child in the group reads at least once. Allocate each group one of the scenes from the play. (Note that Scene 3 has only three characters).

Move from group to group, allocating the scenes and making sure that the parts have been fairly distributed. When you have visited each group, ask the children to begin their readings. Move around the room, monitoring the readings and assisting where necessary. Allow sufficient time for all readings to be completed. If there is enough time after that, ask the groups in sequence to read their scenes aloud to the rest of the class.

Thank the children for their efforts. Ask them to stop reading, turn and face the board again. Move on to...

STORY OUTLINE

WHOLE-CLASS REVIEW AND CONSOLIDATION OF KNOWLEDGE GAINED

Attach a sheet of A3 paper to the board. Write the heading 'Three Murders, a Suicide and a Near Miss' on it. Ask the children to recall the story told in the playscript and to summarize it in sentences which provide a sequential outline of the events.

Prompt their responses by asking: *What is the first important thing that happens in the play?* Record their answer on the paper with a marker pen. Follow this by asking: *What is the next important thing that happens?* Continue in this way until you have the complete story of the play written in the form of a sequential outline.

Take a final moment to confirm with the children that you have recorded all of the important events in the story. Thank the children for their contributions, and retain the story outline for use in the following session.

SESSION 3:
EXPLORING THE STORYLINE

Timing: Spend up to 20 minutes on each activity. The whole session should take no more than 60 minutes.

Resources: A large space (such as the school hall), the A3 story outline sheet from the previous session, chairs (optional).

Objectives: To consolidate knowledge of the play's contents and develop drama skills.

SOUNDTRACKS

PROVIDES A FOCUS FOR RECALL OF THE STORYLINE

Sit with the children in a circle. Invite them to suggest what would be heard if the play were performed in sounds only. Lead the discussion by giving examples: characters walking, characters running, sounds of excitement, sounds of disappointment, and so on. Continue the discussion for a few minutes, and acknowledge all responses.

Arrange the children into seven groups of four to six. Allocate each group a scene from the play. Explain that you want them to perform their scenes using sounds only – no words may be used. (If you feel this is too difficult, allow them to use the words 'yes' and 'no'.) Ask them to read carefully through their scene, and to consider how they could express the action through sounds only. Advise them that their 'soundtracks' need to be prepared, rehearsed and then performed to the class. They can decide for themselves what roles are necessary, and who will play them. Make sure that they all understand what is expected of them.

Allow each group up to 8 minutes to prepare and rehearse their 'scene soundtracks'. Move quickly from group to group, checking that all of the children are working productively and effectively; provide assistance where necessary.

When the rehearsal time limit has elapsed, ask the groups to perform their scene soundtracks in sequence. Lead a brief final discussion on the dramatic effectiveness of the soundtracks and how well they represented the action. Thank the children for their efforts and praise their work, then move quickly on to...

GOSSIP

DEVELOPS USE OF LANGUAGE WITHIN THE STORYLINE CONTEXT

Arrange the children in new groups of five. Ask them to find a space to work in, sitting on chairs or the floor. Explain that they will take on the roles of characters in the play who are gossiping about certain events, using imaginary telephones to talk to each other.

Ask the children in each group to number themselves 1 to 5 (or whatever number is appropriate). Explain that number '1' will start the gossip, passing it by telephone to number '2', who calls number '3', and so on. Tell the children that you will give them the situation for each of their gossip sessions. Make sure that they all understand what is expected of them, then work through the following improvised telephone conversations (or others of your choice):

● MESSENGERS 1, 2 and 3, BRABANTINO and MONTANO gossip about CASSIO being promoted to OTHELLO's deputy. (If there is an extra child, add LODOVICO.)
● IAGO, RODERIGO and GUARDS 1, 2 and 3 gossip about OTHELLO and DESDEMONA getting married. (Add: CASSIO.)

● OTHELLO, IAGO, EMILIA, BIANCA and TIFFANIA gossip about OTHELLO going to war. (Add: DESDEMONA.)
● MESSENGERS 1, 2 and 3, CLOWN and IDIOT gossip about OTHELLO winning the battle against the Turks. (Add: GRATIANO.)
● IAGO, RODERIGO, MONTANO, LODOVICO and GRATIANO gossip about DESDEMONA having an affair with CASSIO. (Add: MESSENGER 3.)
● THE DUKE OF VENICE, CASSIO, MONTANO, LODOVICO and GRATIANO gossip about all the deaths. (Add: MESSENGER 1.)

Allow each group up to 30 seconds preparation time to negotiate their roles. Monitor each improvisation carefully to make sure that all the children have spoken, then move on quickly to the next group.

When each of the improvised conversations has been completed, thank the children for their work and praise their efforts. Ask them to sit in a circle with you, and move quickly on to...

MIMING TO NARRATION

DEVELOPS VERBAL SKILLS AND CONSOLIDATES KNOWLEDGE OF THE PLAY'S CONTENT

Ask the children to recall the story outline of the play that they created at the end of the previous session. Pin up the A3 sheet to confirm their recollections. Say that they are now going to use this story outline to express the play through *narration* and *mime* only. Explain that narration is telling the audience what is happening, and mime is movement without words or sounds.

Ask the children to form new groups of four to six, and to find a space to work in. (Put aside any chairs.) Each group should narrate, in their own words, what happens in a particular section of the story, and accompany the narration with appropriate mimed actions. Explain that they should divide their group into those who will narrate the events and those who will provide the actions. The children miming should take on specific roles. They can have as many narrators as they wish.

Allocate each group up to three consecutive sequential outline sentences from those recorded on the A3 sheet. Ask the children to spend time preparing their narrations and mimes. Advise them to make their narratives brief enough to recall during the performance!

Allow each group up to 8 minutes to devise the narrative and mimes for their outline section. Move quickly from group to group, checking that the children are working productively. When the time limit for preparation and rehearsal has elapsed, ask all of the groups to stop working.

Indicate the order in which the narrated mimes will be performed. Ask each group to perform their narrated mime in turn. Insist that the audience remain silent while each group is performing, and invite them to applaud after each narrated mime.

When the whole story outline has been told in narration and mime, thank the children for their efforts and praise their work. Ask them to sit in a circle with you again, and end with...

CIRCLE

CHILDREN REFLECT ON AND EVALUATE THEIR SKILLS AND KNOWLEDGE

Ask the children whether or not they enjoyed the drama session. Invite opinions and reasons.

● What do they think they have learned and achieved from it?

● What do they feel they have done well? What could they have done better?

● How do they think the activities could help them when they are performing?

● What have they learned about the story of *Three Murders, a Suicide and a Near Miss*?

This gives an indication of any skills and knowledge gained, and can be used as a basis for developing the children's abilities during additional workshop sessions.

SESSION 4:
CHARACTERIZATION AND ROLE-PLAY

Timing: Spend up to 20 minutes on each activity. The whole session should take up to 60 minutes.

Resources: A large space (such as the school hall), chairs.

Objectives: To explore the characters in the play and encourage appropriate use of language in role-play.

TALKING IN TONES
INTRODUCES THE USE OF VOCAL EXPRESSION

Sit with the children in a circle. Say that characters in the play use different *tones of voice* to express their feelings. Invite them to suggest what tones different characters might use. They may suggest: IAGO – angry; RODERIGO – sad; DESDEMONA – afraid; DUKE OF VENICE – shocked. Acknowledge all responses.

Ask the children to find a partner and stand in a space, then label themselves 'A' and 'B'. (Any three can include 'C'.) Explain that you want them to improvise a conversation between two people (not characters from the play) in which one person uses a particular tone of voice. A should begin the conversation by saying, in a shocked tone, 'I'm shocked at you, I really am.' B (and C, if included) should then respond appropriately. Allow these spontaneous enactments to continue for up to 1 minute.

Now ask the children to stop and swap roles, so that B (or C) begins the improvisation with the same line in the same shocked tone of voice. Allow these improvisations to run for up to 1 minute.

Now instruct B to begin a new improvisation: showing off, using a loud voice and starting with the line 'I've just got a new computer, actually...' A (and C) should respond appropriately. Allow these improvised conversations to continue for up to 1 minute; then ask the children to swap roles and repeat the situation for up to a minute.

Now ask the children to enact situations from the play, using specific tones of voice. The situations could include the following (or others of your choice):

● BRABANTINO being shocked about DESDEMONA's intended marriage. (For 'threes' include OTHELLO.)

● MONTANO and LODOVICO reacting with surprise when hearing about DESDEMONA's affair with CASSIO. (For 'threes' include GRATIANO.)

● OTHELLO angrily asking Iago to tell him what he's heard about DESDEMONA. (For 'threes' include RODERIGO.)

When the children have enacted as many different conversations as time allows, thank them for their efforts. Ask them to find a new partner and a new space, then move on to...

WHAT WE SAY AND WHAT WE THINK
LINKS VOCAL EXPRESSION TO CHARACTERIZATION

Ask the children to sit down with their new partners. Invite them to suggest moments in the play when characters are *saying* one thing, but *thinking* something different. Use the character of Iago as an illustration: we hear his thoughts spoken to us, but also hear how he says different things to other characters. Acknowledge all suggestions, praising those that are particularly insightful or well-considered.

Explain that you want the children to work with their partners to improvise situations where a character is saying one thing, but thinking something entirely different. Examples could include the following (or others suggested by you or the children):

● IAGO being pleasant to CASSIO, while feeling jealous.

● EMILIA being polite to TIFFANIA, while feeling irritated.

● RODERIGO agreeing to help IAGO, while feeling afraid and uncertain.

● OTHELLO being nice to DESDEMONA, while feeling that he wants to kill her.

Ask the pairs to label themselves 'A' and 'B', then improvise a conversation between characters where one character is saying one thing and thinking something else. (For threes, the teacher could work with the remaining child.) Allow the improvisation to continue for up to 1 minute, then ask the children to swap roles and repeat the conversation, again for up to a minute.

Let the pairs work through three or four different conversations in this way. Use any remaining time to hear three or four of the conversations, asking pairs to perform an improvisation in front of the others. Lead a brief discussion about how realistic the portrayal of each character was, how effective the use of vocal expression was, and so on.

Thank all of the children for their efforts and praise their work. Ask them to find a new partner and a new space, and move quickly on to...

RADIO INTERVIEWS

CONSOLIDATES VERBAL CHARACTERIZATION

Ask the children to sit on chairs, facing their partners, and to label themselves 'A' and 'B'. (Any three can include 'C'.) Explain that A is a disc jockey working for a local radio station, and that he or she is interviewing characters from the play. The children will have to improvise radio interviews spontaneously, without preparation.

Say that the child playing the role of the disc jockey should begin the improvisation by saying: 'And now, I'm pleased to welcome onto the show...' and then naming one of the characters from the play. B must then adopt the role of the character named. (C should be introduced as a different character, and must adopt that role.) A must remain in role, asking the character played by B (or B and C) questions about his or her life and how he or she reacted to certain events in the play. These events are, again, specified by the child playing the disc jockey.

Allow these radio interviews to continue for up to two minutes. Move around the room, listening to the children's improvisations and commenting positively on them (in particular, praising those children who are sustaining their roles well).

Now ask the children to swap roles, so that B (or B and C) now becomes the disc jockey and A becomes a different character in the play. Repeat the process, listening to the interviews and commenting positively on them. Allow these radio interviews to continue for up to 2 minutes.

If time allows, ask the children to swap roles again, selecting yet another character from the play as interviewee.

When the time limit for this exercise has elapsed, thank the children for their efforts and praise their work. Ask them to sit in a circle with you again, and end with...

CIRCLE

CHILDREN REFLECT ON AND EVALUATE THEIR SKILLS AND KNOWLEDGE

Ask the children whether or not they enjoyed the drama session. Invite opinions and reasons.

- What do they think they have learned and achieved from it?
- What do they feel they have done well? What could they have done better?
- How do they think the activities could help them when they are performing?
- What have they learned in this drama session about the characters in *Three Murders, a Suicide and a Near Miss*?

This discussion gives an indication of any skills and knowledge gained, and can be used as a basis for developing the children's abilities during additional workshop sessions.

SESSION 5:
CONSOLIDATING PERFORMANCE SKILLS

Timing: Spend up to 20 minutes on each activity. The whole session should take no more than 60 minutes.

Resources: A large space (such as the school hall), the sequential story outline from Session 2, copies of the playscript; chairs (optional), A3 paper and pen (optional).

Objectives: To consolidate knowledge of the play and concentrate performance skills.

DRAMATIC PAUSES

ENCOURAGES CHILDREN TO RESPOND APPROPRIATELY AND IN UNISON

Ask the children to stand in a circle. Invite them to suggest moments in the play when characters might speak in unison: two or more people saying the same thing at the same time. Acknowledge all responses.

Explain that you want the children to learn how to respond in unison, and to do so in a dramatic way that creates tension. Tell them that pauses after speech can be very expressive when performed effectively and dramatically. Make sure that all the children are silent and concentrating. Tell them that you want them all to say 'No!' together and then keep completely quiet. Ask them to concentrate hard on responding together. *Are you ready? Three, two, one – go!*

Make appropriate positive comments about the children's response to your instructions. Now tell them that you want them to imagine they are about to be crushed by a huge falling rock. They all need to shout 'No!' in unison. Ask whether they are ready, then give the *Three, two, one* countdown and the command

'Go!' Respond positively again (if appropriate), encouraging the children to remain completely silent after they have responded in unison.

Now tell the children that you want them to imagine they are all teachers, noticing someone going into the school who shouldn't be there. Ask them to shout 'Stop!' together. Make sure they are ready, then give the countdown and the 'Go!' command. Praise and encourage appropriately, reiterating the need for a dramatic pause after the response.

Finally, with whatever time remains, repeat the process using other expressive words such as 'Hey!', 'Help!', 'Go!' or 'You!'

Thank the children for their efforts, praise their work and move on to...

STORYLINE IMPROVISATIONS
CONSOLIDATES KNOWLEDGE OF THE TEXT AND DEVELOPS PERFORMANCE SKILLS

Arrange the children in groups of five to eight. Tell them that you want them to work in their groups to develop and perform improvisations of different sections of the story of *Three Murders, a Suicide and a Near Miss*. They should use *actions* (movement) and *dialogue* (speech) to bring their section of the story to life. The dialogue should be improvised in their own words. These improvisations of the sections will then be performed in turn to give a version of the whole play.

Using the story outline sheet from Session 2, allocate up to three of the sequential sentences to each group. Check that all the children are clear about which sentences have been allocated to their group and what they have to do.

Allow the groups up to 5 minutes to plan and rehearse their storyline improvisations. Warn them of this time limit. After this time, ask the groups to perform their storyline improvisations in sequence to the class. Encourage the audience to remain silent while watching, and invite them to applaud after each performance.

When the entire storyline has been acted out in this way, thank the children for their efforts and praise their work. Move quickly on to...

SCRIPT EXTRACTS

REINTRODUCES THE PLAYSCRIPT AND PREPARES CHILDREN FOR FORMAL PERFORMANCE

Tell the children that you are going to ask them to perform sections of the playscript aloud to each other. Explain that their performances can either be simple readings or include actions.

Distribute copies of the script, retaining one for yourself. Arrange the children in groups, preferably of mixed reading ability, and allocate script extracts. Tell the children that some of them will have to speak the lines for more than one character. Whether their performance is static or moved, they should use vocal and facial expressions. Remind the children of any previous workshop experience that might help them to do this.

The extracts could be as follows (or make your own selections):

- Three to five children: Scene 1.
- Three to six children: Scene 2.
- Three children: Scene 3.
- Three to six children: Scene 4.
- Three to five children: Scene 5.
- Three to five children: Scene 6.
- Four to eight children: Scene 7.

Allow the children up to 8 minutes to read and rehearse their script extracts. Move quickly from group to group, making sure that the parts have been distributed fairly and all the children are working productively.

When the planning and rehearsal time has elapsed, ask the groups to perform their script extracts in sequence. Insist on silence from the audience members while other groups are performing, and invite the audience to applaud after each performance.

When the entire play has been performed, thank the children for their work and praise their efforts. Ask them to sit in a circle with you, and end with...

CIRCLE

CHILDREN REFLECT ON AND EVALUATE THEIR SKILLS AND KNOWLEDGE

Ask the children if they enjoyed the drama session. Invite opinions and reasons.

- Which aspects did they enjoy the most and the least?
- What do they think they have learned or achieved from the session?
- What do they feel is the most important skill they have learned?
- What do they feel they have done well? What could they have done better?
- How do they feel about their performances?
- What would they change or do better if they had the chance to perform again?
- What do they feel is the most important thing to remember when performing in front of others?

Acknowledge all responses. Finally, thank the children for their hard work and praise their efforts. You may wish to record the children's answers on an A3 sheet of paper to provide a visual prompt during rehearsals of the play.

Three Murders, a Suicide and a Near Miss

CAST LIST

Announcer/Narrator	Clown
Iago	Idiot
Roderigo	Tiffania
Cassio	Guard 1
Brabantino	Guard 2
Othello	Guard 3
Desdemona	Messenger 1
The Duke of Venice	Messenger 2
Bianca	Messenger 3
Emilia	
Montano	There are 22
	characters. There
Lodovico	may also be two
	Prison Officers
Gratiano	(non-speaking parts)
	in the final scene.

SCENES

1 Othello's garrison
2 Outside Brabantino's house
3 Bianca's house
4 In the town square
5 In a different part of the town, some time later
6 In the town square
7 Othello's and Desdemona's house

Photocopiable

CHARACTER OUTLINES

Announcer/Narrator: Introduces and closes the play, linking it to the audience.

Iago: A nasty villain, evil and jealous, who seeks revenge.

Roderigo: A gentle but quite stupid man who is in love with Desdemona.

Cassio: An irritatingly cheerful, kind and trusting soldier.

Messenger 1: An excitable news-teller who loves to gossip.

Messenger 2: A spoilsport news-teller who is generally bored.

Messenger 3: A bad-tempered news-teller who is regularly miserable.

Guard 1: An overworked soldier with a spiteful nature.

Guard 2: A stupid overworked soldier.

Guard 3: A cheerful overworked soldier.

Brabantino: A rich old man and Desdemona's devoted father.

Othello: The hero. Old, good and loyal, but with a dangerously jealous nature.

Desdemona: The heroine. Rich, beautiful, lovely and loyal.

Bianca: A silly young woman. Girlfriend of Cassio.

Emilia: Friend of Bianca and Tiffania, wife of Iago. Honest, good and kind.

Tiffania: Bianca's best friend. A silly young woman who fancies Roderigo.

Montano: An important official who likes to be involved with events.

Lodovico: Another important official with a special talent for stating the obvious!

Gratiano: A third important official, with a nosy and gossipy nature.

Clown: The 'village idiot'.

Idiot: The 'village clown'.

The Duke of Venice: Ruler of the town. A wise old man who doesn't tolerate fools.

Photocopiable

The ANNOUNCER enters in front of the closed curtains.

ANNOUNCER: Ladies and Gentlemen! We would like to present to you our dramatic tale of love, jealousy and revenge. Steel yourselves against the evil acts of our villain, revel in the antics of our comic characters and prepare to shed tears over the misunderstandings of unrequited love. We have heroines to beguile you, heroes to warm the cockles of your heart, idiots to amuse you and a villain to make you jeer and boo until your throat is sore! Please be reassured that none of these characters are based on real people – this is simply the magic of theatre. I give you our humble dramatic offering, entitled *Three Murders, a Suicide and a Near Miss* – or *Othello*. Thank you.

The curtains open.

SCENE 1: **Othello's garrison**

OTHELLO, CASSIO and IAGO are on stage.

OTHELLO: Cassio! Iago! My true and faithful officers. I have some good news and some bad news.

CASSIO: What's the good news, Othello?

OTHELLO: One of you is to be promoted to be my second-in-command.

IAGO: And the bad news?

OTHELLO: One of you isn't.

CASSIO: Tell us! Tell us! Who will it be, Othello? *(To Iago)* I bet it isn't me.

OTHELLO: Then you would lose your bet, good Cassio, for it *is* you!

CASSIO: *(clapping his hands excitedly)* Hurrah!

Photocopiable

IAGO: *(disappointedly)* Oh.

OTHELLO: Do not despair, Iago, for I have a special job for you too.

IAGO: Yes?

OTHELLO: You shall be my standard-bearer and carry the official flag.

IAGO: *(trying to sound pleased)* Wonderful!

CASSIO: I must go immediately and tell Bianca! *(He exits.)*

OTHELLO: I too must go. Chin up, Iago, one day your turn will come.

(Othello exits.)

IAGO: *(to audience)* Chin up? How *could* Othello promote that idiot Cassio and overlook me? I am strong, resourceful, loyal – and evil! I will *not* spend my life wandering about with bits of cloth! Cassio must go and I will have my revenge! *(He swishes his cloak round menacingly.)*

MESSENGER 1 runs in.
MESSENGER 2 wanders in a few moments later.

MESSENGER 1: Iago! Iago! Have you heard the news? Cassio has been promoted to Othello's deputy!

IAGO: *(dismissively)* I know, I know. Don't speak to me of it.

MESSENGER 1: *(disappointed)* Oh. *(But brightening up)* Well, have you heard the other news?

IAGO: What? What?

MESSENGER 2: *(has just entered)* Othello and Desdemona have just got married.

MESSENGER 1: *(upset and annoyed)* I wanted to tell him that.

IAGO: What? Married? This is *too* much. Leave! Leave!

Photocopiable

The MESSENGERS exit.

IAGO: Othello has everything now – a faithful deputy, a beautiful wife, loyal friends. I cannot bear this. Why should heaven smile on him and frown on me? I will think of a dastardly plan to upset their happiness and dispose of that idiot Cassio! My time will come!

IAGO exits, laughing in an evil manner.
RODERIGO enters from the opposite side of the stage, carrying a flower.

RODERIGO: *(pulling petals off flower)* She loves me, she loves me not, she loves me, she loves me not. *(He sits.)* Oh, Desdemona! Why have you forsaken me and wed another? Why are the brightest jewels never fixed to the dullest crowns? Oh, Desdemona, I love you with all my heart, and would give all that I have for just one smile from your sainted lips. *(He jumps as IAGO enters.)* Iago!

IAGO: On your feet, Roderigo, we have serious talking to do.

RODERIGO: Leave me be, Iago. I am in pain.

IAGO: *(threateningly)* Not yet you aren't. On your feet!

RODERIGO stands.

IAGO: Cassio has been promoted and it should have been me! I work hard, but he has the friends in high places. I intend to find a way to remove Cassio – and you, Roderigo, will help me.

RODERIGO: Me?

IAGO: *(correcting him)* I.

RODERIGO: Sorry, I?

IAGO: Yes, you.

RODERIGO: What? Help you to overthrow Cassio and have him removed from his position?

IAGO: That's what I just said, didn't I?

RODERIGO: Oh. Right. He's quite stupid, isn't he? He's also handsome and pleasant and noble and loyal and honest... and... and...

IAGO: ...Stop! His stupidity also makes him naïve. It will be easy to discredit him and then I, the magnificent Iago, can step into his place.

RODERIGO: Oh. Good. But...

IAGO: ...Go now, Roderigo, and meet me outside Brabantino's house in an hour. I have some serious thinking to do while I form my dastardly plan!

RODERIGO exits.
IAGO exits, laughing nastily.

SCENE 2: **Outside Brabantino's house**

GUARD 1, GUARD 2 and GUARD 3 are standing on stage, on night guard duty for Brabantino.

GUARD 1: What time is it?

GUARD 2: Ten minutes later than when you last asked me.

GUARD 1: And what time was it then?

GUARD 2: I don't know, watches haven't been invented yet.

GUARD 3: My feet are killing me. Couldn't we sit down for a while?

GUARD 2: No. We're paid to stand guard, and that means standing.

Photocopiable

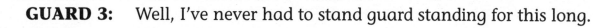

GUARD 3:   Well, I've never had to stand guard standing for this long.

GUARD 1:   I know, fourteen hours and still no sign of rest.

GUARD 2:   I wish I'd chosen another career. My mother said I could have been anything I wanted to be.

GUARD 3:   Your mother said a lot of things. She also said that leeches were an excellent cure for toothache.

GUARD 2:   Yes, well, she was just a forward thinker, that's all.

GUARD 1:   A fruitcake, more like.

GUARD 2:   You take that back, or else!

GUARD 1:   All right, your mother was not a fruitcake.

GUARD 2:   Good.

GUARD 1:   *(aside to the audience)* And if you believe that, you're a bigger fruitcake than she is.

There is a long pause.

GUARD 3:   What time is it? Is it nearly home time?

GUARD 2:   *(Looking at the sky)* No. It's still night and, as we're on night duty, I assume we stay here until it isn't night.

GUARD 3:   Fancy a game of I-Spy?

GUARD 2:   Go on, then.

GUARD 3:   I spy, with my little eye, something beginning with... Iago!

GUARD 1:   Beginning with Iago? That doesn't make sense!

GUARD 3:   No! Iago – over there – coming this way.

GUARD 2:   Oh no, there goes our quiet night.

Photocopiable

IAGO enters.

IAGO: Gentlemen! I wish to speak with Brabantino.

GUARD 1:   He's asleep.

RODERIGO enters.

IAGO: I must speak with him now! It is a matter of national emergency.

GUARD 2:   *(looking at the others, who nod)* Oh, well, that's different then.

The GUARDS, RODERIGO and IAGO shout and make lots of noise.

ALL TOGETHER: *(ad-libbing)* Brabantino! Brabantino! Sir! Sir! We have news of Desdemona! *(Etc.)*

BRABANTINO eventually enters, rubbing his eyes sleepily.

BRABANTINO: What is all this noise? Why all the pandemonium? You say you have news of my daughter, the young and beautiful Desdemona? Tell me at once!

IAGO: The young and beautiful Desdemona has, this very night, slipped away from her maidenly chamber within your house and has become the wife of... Othello!

BRABANTINO: *(swoons slightly)* It cannot be so! My lovely daughter, the young and beautiful Desdemona, the young and beautiful and *rich* Desdemona, married to that old and poor but honest usurper Othello? Tell me it's not true.

RODERIGO: *(upset)* It is true, Brabantino, the news – which also pierces like an arrow through my heart – is all over town.

BRABANTINO: Fetch them to me! Bring me Othello and Desdemona now – this minute!

Photocopiable

GUARD 1 exits to fetch DESDEMONA and OTHELLO.

GUARD 2:   *(to GUARD 3)* He is not a happy man.

GUARD 3:   *(agreeing cheerfully)* No. This should liven things up a bit.

IAGO: *(to the audience, aside)* I have started my dastardly plan, and will soon have spread the unhappiness and distress that I so desire.

GUARD 1 enters with DESDEMONA, OTHELLO, MESSENGER 1, MESSENGER 2 and MESSENGER 3.

DESDEMONA: Father?

BRABANTINO: Desdemona?

DESDEMONA: Father!

BRABANTINO: Desdemona! *(He pauses, in pain)* It is true, then, that you have broken your poor father's heart by marrying this... this... *(he can't think of a suitable word)* ...man!

OTHELLO: I'll get me coat.

BRABANTINO: Stay right there! Explain yourself!

OTHELLO: Well, I love her and she loves me.

EVERYONE IN UNISON: *(Except Desdemona and Othello)* Love! Pah!

BRABANTINO: Desdemona, my beautiful, young, lovely daughter. What can you see in him? He's old enough to be your... *(pause)* ...much older brother.

DESDEMONA: I love him, father.

EVERYONE IN UNISON: *(Except Desdemona and Othello)* Love! Pah!

Photocopiable

BRABANTINO: But to sneak away and marry without my say-so! It almost makes me want to cry. *(He swoons dramatically.)*

DESDEMONA: I'm sorry, father.

OTHELLO: We're sorry, fath... er... Brabantino.

BRABANTINO: *(ignoring Othello)* You could have had your pick of any of the young men. Why him? Why have you done this to me?

DESDEMONA: I know he is much older than me, but we think the same way, we feel the same things. I love Othello with all my heart, and he loves me completely too.

RODERIGO: *(thinking that everyone else will join in – they don't)* Love! Pah! *(He looks embarrassed.)*

EVERYONE EXCEPT BRABANTINO freezes in position.

BRABANTINO: *(to the audience)* I do believe that these young people are honest and true in their feelings for each other and, though it breaks my heart, I must give them my blessing.

EVERYONE unfreezes.

BRABANTINO: *(To Othello and Desdemona)* You have my blessing.

EVERYONE cheers, except IAGO and RODERIGO.
DESDEMONA and OTHELLO hug each other happily.

DESDEMONA: Oh, thank you, father! Now we can celebrate our nuptials.

BRABANTINO: *(embarrassed)* Yes, well, plenty of time for that. Let's get some sleep first, shall we? Back to bed, everyone.

EVERYONE exits except IAGO and RODERIGO, who remain on stage together.

RODERIGO: *(very upset)* Oh, why did she forsake me and choose him? I would have given her anything her heart desired. Everything that she might wish for, she would have had.

Photocopiable

IAGO: *(aside to the audience)* Except for meaningful, intelligent conversation. *(To Roderigo)* Go to bed, Roderigo. Things always look better in the morning.

RODERIGO exits, singing a sad love song to himself as he goes.

IAGO: Curses! My plan to upset Othello has failed. Now is the time for serious plotting. Cassio has upset me, and Othello has upset my friend. Revenge must be mine! I will spread the completely believable rumour that Cassio and Desdemona are having an affair. Othello is a very jealous man, and soon he will have abandoned Desdemona and sacked Cassio – and revenge *will* be mine!

IAGO exits, laughing nastily as he goes.

SCENE 3: **Bianca's house**

BIANCA, EMILIA and TIFFANIA are sitting together, gossiping.

EMILIA: *(to BIANCA)* You must be so proud of Cassio's new promotion, Bianca.

BIANCA: Oh, yes. It's nice to have a boyfriend in high places.

TIFFANIA: *(to EMILIA)* Has Iago been promoted too, Emilia?

EMILIA: You know very well that he hasn't, Tiffania.

TIFFANIA: I was only asking.

BIANCA: Oh, give it a rest, Tiff.

TIFFANIA: What do you think about Desdemona and Othello, then?

BIANCA: Well, I think it's disgusting. He's far too old for her.

EMILIA: I don't think that matters if you love someone, does it?

Three Murders, a Suicide and a Near Miss

Three Murders,
A Suicide and
A Near Miss

BIANCA: Love! Pah!

TIFFANIA: *(sighing)* Well, I think it's really romantic. I wish Roderigo would propose to me.

EMILIA: It's not going to happen, Tiffania. Iago tells me he's madly in love with Desdemona.

TIFFANIA: I know, I know. How could he fancy her when he could have me?

BIANCA and EMILIA exchange glances about this.

EMILIA: Iago says that Othello's going to war and Desdemona's going with him.

BIANCA: Perhaps she won't return. Then the path will be clear for you and Roderigo.

TIFFANIA: Yes, I'll be able to console him in his grief.

EMILIA: Is Cassio going too?

BIANCA: Of course he is! He's Othello's deputy.

EMILIA: *(showing off)* I've been appointed as Desdemona's maid, so I'll be going – and, of course, Iago will be keeping her out of danger.

TIFFANIA: *(as if EMILIA's said something rude)* Oooh!

EMILIA AND BIANCA IN UNISON: Oh, give it a rest, Tiff!

Photocopiable

SCENE 4: **In the town square**

CLOWN (the village idiot) enters.

CLOWN: *(to the audience)* I am Clown, the village idiot. With a jolly jest and a quirky quip I fool about all day.

IDIOT (the village clown) enters.

IDIOT: *(to the audience)* I am Idiot, the village clown. With a jolly jest...

CLOWN: *(interrupting)* ...I've done that.

IDIOT: Oh. *(Thinks)* With mirthful merriment and foolish frippery I always bring good cheer. *(He looks at CLOWN with a superior expression on his face.)*

CLOWN: Idiot, I have a jolly jest for thee! When is a wise man like an idiot?

IDIOT: Pray, tell me, good Clown.

CLOWN: When he is stupid!

They both laugh hysterically at this and hit each other repeatedly with 'pig bladders' on sticks.

IDIOT: *(still gasping with laughter)* Your foolishness makes my sides split. Tell me, Clown, why is the sun like an orange?

CLOWN: I do not know.

IDIOT: Because they are both round!

They both fall about hysterically again, hitting each other with 'pig bladders' on sticks.

CLOWN: *(gasping with laughter)* Oh, stop! Stop! This merriment will be the undoing of me!

IDIOT: One more, one more. When is a door not a door?

CLOWN: *(still laughing from the previous joke)* Tell me! Tell me!

IDIOT: When it's a jar! *(He starts laughing.)*

CLOWN: *(stops laughing immediately)* That's not funny.

IDIOT: *(also stops laughing)* No, it isn't, is it?

They both stand there feeling awkward, hitting each other with no enthusiasm and trying to laugh.
MONTANO, LODOVICO and GRATIANO enter. CLOWN and IDIOT bow to them.

CLOWN: Good day, honoured Montano, Lodovico and Gratiano. Can we cajole thee to laughter?

IDIOT: We have jokes and japes and quips and merriment. What will thy pleasure be?

MONTANO: Nothing today, thank you.

CLOWN: Fair enough.

MESSENGERS 1, 2 and 3 enter.

MESSENGER 3: Good day, honoured Montano, Lodovico and Gratiano! Good day, Clown! Good day, Idiot! The Messengers bring you news.

MESSENGER 1: I thought you said it was my turn!

MESSENGER 3: *(to MESSENGER 1)* You took too long. *(To the others)* We have news and we have gossip. Which would you like first?

LODOVICO: News.

MESSENGER 2: Othello and his army have won the battle against the Turks.

Everyone cheers.

Photocopiable

MESSENGER 3:   We have more news or gossip. What is your preference?

GRATIANO: More news.

MESSENGER 2:   Brabantino has died.

EVERYONE IN UNISON: *(sadly)* Aaah.

LODOVICO: And the gossip?

MESSENGER 1:   *(speaking quickly before anyone else can)* There's a rumour going around that Cassio and Desdemona are having an affair.

EVERYONE IN UNISON: *(Except the MESSENGERS)* No!

MONTANO: I can't believe it!

GRATIANO: I don't believe it!

LODOVICO: I won't believe it! Surely there is some mistake?

MESSENGER 2:   No, no mistake. I heard it myself with my own ears.

GRATIANO: Oh, well then, it must be true.

MONTANO: Come, Lodovico and Gratiano, we must do our duty.

GRATIANO: Yes, we must spread this gossip far and wide.

LODOVICO: Indeed. Come, gentlemen.

MONTANO, LODOVICO and GRATIANO exit quickly.

CLOWN: *(to the MESSENGERS)* Would you like a merry quip?

MESSENGER 3:   *(politely)* No thank you.

Photocopiable

IDIOT: All right. *(To CLOWN)* Let's go and irritate the Duke of Venice. He's far too noble to ask us to leave.

CLOWN: *(nodding)* Good idea.

CLOWN and IDIOT exit.
MESSENGERS 1, 2 and 3 exit together in a different direction, chatting to each other about the gossip.

SCENE 5: **In a different part of the town, some time later**

IAGO enters.

IAGO: My plan has begun. I will spread my evil until I have achieved my aim – to destroy Cassio and Othello! Othello is already in doubt about the young and lovely Desdemona. Now I must finish Cassio. Look! Here he comes.

CASSIO enters.

CASSIO: Good day, Iago.

IAGO: Good day, Cassio. Congratulations on winning the battle against the Turks. Are you coming to the celebration party?

CASSIO: No. I'm not much for all that drinking and singing. I think I'll just go to bed with a good book.

IAGO: Oh, come on, you can have one little drink. Can't you?

CASSIO: *(protesting)* No, really, Iago, I can't take it. I behave completely out of character after a drink.

IAGO looks knowingly at the audience.

IAGO: *(smiling insidiously)* Oh, really? It seems awful, though, to shun your soldiers by not celebrating with them. Perhaps you could force yourself to have just a little one, watered down?

RODERIGO enters.

CASSIO: *(doubtfully)* I don't know. It wouldn't be very sensible of me. *(He pauses.)* Maybe I'll just go and thank them for all their hard work, though.

CASSIO exits.

IAGO: *(excitedly)* I have him! The soldiers have been given their instructions! Now, Roderigo, it is time for you to play your part in my... er, our... plan to get rid of Cassio. He will get roaring drunk, and you are to pick a fight with him.

RODERIGO: What about?

IAGO: It doesn't matter! Anything. Just start an argument, all right?

RODERIGO: All right.

IAGO: And keep it going until Othello arrives.

RODERIGO: How do you know that Othello will arrive?

IAGO: He will, trust me.

A loud, drunken row is heard offstage – coming from the direction of CASSIO's exit.

IAGO: That was quick! Off you go, Roderigo.

RODERIGO exits towards the noise and can be heard shouting insults at CASSIO offstage.
IAGO exits quickly in the opposite direction, returning immediately with OTHELLO and MONTANO.
Suddenly, CASSIO chases RODERIGO onto the stage and attacks him violently. MONTANO separates them.

Photocopiable

OTHELLO: *(furiously)* Cassio! What is this? You are drunk and being very disorderly. I cannot tolerate this type of behaviour in my senior officer. You are sacked from your position with immediate effect! *(To MONTANO)* Take him away, Montano. He has disappointed me greatly.

MONTANO leads a loudly protesting CASSIO offstage.
IAGO signals quietly to RODERIGO that he should leave. RODERIGO exits quickly.

IAGO: What a shame! He seemed such a dependable man. Still, I have been hearing certain things about him that, quite frankly, make me blush.

OTHELLO: What things?

IAGO: I couldn't possibly tell you.

OTHELLO: Yes, you could.

IAGO: No, I couldn't. I don't believe in telling tales.

OTHELLO: Tell me, Iago, what have you heard?

IAGO: It's only gossip and hearsay.

OTHELLO: *(Shouting angrily)* IAGO! As a true and loyal friend, TELL ME WHAT YOU KNOW ABOUT CASSIO!

IAGO: Well, have you not noticed how friendly he has become with your wife, the young and lovely Desdemona?

OTHELLO: No.

IAGO: Oh well, that's all right then.

OTHELLO: Has he?

IAGO: Has he what?

OTHELLO: Become friendly with the young and lovely Desdemona?

Photocopiable

Three Murders,
a Suicide and
a Near Miss

IAGO: Yes. So I've heard, anyway.

OTHELLO: *(overacting madly)* I knew it! I knew it was too good to be true. She would never stay faithful to me! She was too young and lovely, and I am too old and boring for her. Oh woe is me! Oh Desdemona! Oh Cassio! *(Pauses, then nastily)* I'll kill him!

IAGO: No, Othello, I'll kill him.

OTHELLO: Thank you, good Iago, my true and faithful friend. *(He pauses, thinking.)* Then I'll kill her.

IAGO: Don't you want more proof?

OTHELLO: No! Why would you lie? *(Pauses to think.)* But then again, what if it's untrue? Yes, maybe I should seek more proof.

IAGO: I have it. *(He brings out the handkerchief.)*

OTHELLO: What is this? That is the handkerchief that I gave to Desdemona during our courtship! It is a family heirloom, and was a special symbol of our love. Where did you find it?

IAGO: In Cassio's chamber.

OTHELLO: *(swooning and getting hysterical again)* Oh woe is me! Oh Desdemona, how could you? How could you forsake our love for the arms of another? Oh Cassio, how could you betray our friendship in such a heinous manner? Oh sorrow! Oh pain!

IAGO: *(to the audience)* Oh what terrible overacting! *(To Othello)* Don't worry, Othello, I shall ease your suffering by disposing of Cassio – tonight!

OTHELLO: I must deal with my young and lovely wife. Thank you, Iago, for your loyalty. Oh woe! Oh pain! Oh sorrow!

Photocopiable

IAGO and OTHELLO exit in opposite directions.
DESDEMONA enters from the opposite side of the stage to where OTHELLO
has just exited.
OTHELLO enters again.

DESDEMONA: *(pleased to see him)* Othello! What a lovely surprise! I want to have a word with you about Cassio.

OTHELLO: *(sarcastically)* Yes, I bet you do.

DESDEMONA: He begged me to speak to you. He is distraught and assures me he will never get drunk again.

OTHELLO: *(nastily)* Is that all he begged you for?

DESDEMONA: *(puzzled)* What *do* you mean?

OTHELLO: I mean that you seem very keen to put Cassio's case all of a sudden. Now why is that?

DESDEMONA: Because he asked me to. *(She pauses, confused.)* What is wrong, Othello? Why do you look so fierce?

OTHELLO: *(wiping his brow with his hand)* I'm not feeling myself. Pass me your handkerchief, Desdemona.

DESDEMONA: Erm...

OTHELLO: Your handkerchief, please, Desdemona. The one that I gave you as a special gift.

DESDEMONA: I... I... It's...

OTHELLO: You don't have it, do you?

DESDEMONA: No. It is true, I have misplaced it.

OTHELLO: Where did you lose it? Was it in your room? Was it in the street? Was it in Cassio's chamber?

DESDEMONA:	Cassio's chamber? I don't understand. Othello, you're making me afraid.
OTHELLO:	You have betrayed me, Desdemona.
DESDEMONA:	No!
OTHELLO:	Yes!
DESDEMONA:	No, no, Othello!
OTHELLO:	Yes, yes, Des! I'll deal with you later.

---

*OTHELLO exits angrily, leaving DESDEMONA distressed and weeping
alone on the stage.
After a few seconds, DESDEMONA exits.*

SCENE 6: **In the town square**

IAGO and RODERIGO enter.

RODERIGO:	This feels all wrong, Iago.
IAGO:	Do you hate Othello?
RODERIGO:	Yes, of course. He married the young and lovely Desdemona, whom I adore.
IAGO:	Right! And do you hate Cassio?
RODERIGO:	Of course. He is having an affair with the young and lovely Desdemona, whom I adore.
IAGO:	And he took the job that was rightfully mine.
RODERIGO:	(agreeing quickly) And he took the job that was rightfully yours.
IAGO:	Then we must get rid of Cassio once and for all – agreed?

Photocopiable

RODERIGO: Agreed! *(Pauses, working it out.)* Which means...?

IAGO: Tonight, good Roderigo, is your lucky night! For you shall kill Cassio.

RODERIGO: *(fearfully)* Not me!

IAGO: Yes, you! I shall be close by to provide support, naturally. We will wait here by this shop and, when Cassio appears just after midnight, you will jump on him and attack him until he is dead!

RODERIGO: What? Stab him?

IAGO: Stab, strangle – it doesn't really matter how, just kill him. Just picture him and the young and lovely Desdemona together, and you'll find it very easy.

RODERIGO: *(nobly)* I shall kill him for her honour!

IAGO: Whatever. Now we wait until just after midnight.

They position themselves in hiding by a 'shop' and freeze.
A CHARACTER walks onto the stage and says to the audience: 'Just after midnight.'
He or she then exits immediately on the opposite side of the stage.
RODERIGO and IAGO unfreeze.
CASSIO enters. RODERIGO leaps out at him with his sword.

RODERIGO: *(shouting)* Cassio! Prepare to die.

CASSIO is confused, but reacts instinctively. He draws his sword and fights with RODERIGO.
While the sword fight is happening, IAGO creeps offstage.
Finally, CASSIO stabs RODERIGO.

RODERIGO: You have stabbed me! I am slain! I am slain!

As he collapses to the ground, RODERIGO stabs CASSIO in the leg.

CASSIO: You have stabbed me! I am lame! I am lame!

Photocopiable

RODERIGO: Help! Help! I die!

CASSIO: Help! Help! I am wounded! I am bleeding!

IAGO enters again, with MONTANO, LODOVICO and GRATIANO.

IAGO: What is all this noise?

GRATIANO: *(going to CASSIO)* It is Cassio, he is wounded!

MONTANO: It is Cassio, he is bleeding!

LODOVICO: Who did this terrible deed? Who was your attacker?

IAGO: *(sees Roderigo)* Here is his attacker! I will halt his evil ways.

IAGO stabs RODERIGO and kills him.

RODERIGO: *(in surprise and shock)* I am killed!

GRATIANO: *(to IAGO)* You have saved Cassio.

MONTANO: You have protected us!

LODOVICO: *(pausing and looking at the victim, then in surprise)* You've killed Roderigo!

MONTANO: Hurry! Let us go quickly to Othello and tell him the news of Cassio and Roderigo!

GRATIANO: Yes, hurry!

They all begin to exit.

CASSIO: *(shouting after them)* Wait! What about me? I am wounded, I am bleeding!

They all return, drag RODERIGO's body offstage on one side, then lift CASSIO up and carry him offstage on the opposite side.

Photocopiable

SCENE 7: **Othello's and Desdemona's house**

DESDEMONA is lying in bed.
OTHELLO enters.

OTHELLO: *(nastily)* You have one more chance, my young and lovely wife, to tell me the truth.

DESDEMONA: *(fearfully)* I am not lying, Othello! I have no love for Cassio. May God strike me down dead if I am not telling you the truth.

OTHELLO: God will not kill you, my beautiful Desdemona, but I will.

OTHELLO strangles DESDEMONA dramatically.
DESDEMONA chokes – also dramatically – but does not die immediately.
Suddenly EMILIA, IAGO, MONTANO, BIANCA, TIFFANIA, LODOVICO and GRATIANO all rush in.
EMILIA hurries over to DESDEMONA.

EMILIA: My mistress! *(To OTHELLO accusingly)* What has happened to her?

DESDEMONA: *(in a strained voice)* He has slain me, Emilia.

EMILIA: Who?

DESDEMONA: Oth...

EVERYONE IN UNISON: *(Except OTHELLO)* Yes?

DESDEMONA: Oth...

EVERYONE IN UNISON: *(Except OTHELLO)* Yes?

DESDEMONA: Othello.

DESDEMONA dies dramatically.
EVERYONE turns and looks accusingly at OTHELLO.

Photocopiable

OTHELLO: She betrayed me with another. She forsook me for Cassio.

EMILIA: Fool! My mistress had no love for Cassio. Who told you this story?

OTHELLO: Iago, my true and honest friend.

EVERYONE turns and looks accusingly at IAGO.

OTHELLO: He found her handkerchief in Cassio's chamber.

EMILIA: Idiot!

IDIOT rushes on stage.

EVERYONE IN UNISON: *(shouting to IDIOT)* Not you!

IDIOT exits quickly.

EMILIA: Iago did not find that handkerchief. I did, and gave it to him at his request.

OTHELLO: *(crestfallen)* Oh!

EMILIA: My husband has done you wrong, Othello. He has lied to you and given you false tales, and he has brought about this terrible end. *(Wailing sorrowfully)* Oh, my poor mistress!

OTHELLO: *(wailing even louder)* Oh, my poor young and lovely Desdemona! *(To Iago angrily)* You fiend!

IAGO: *(to Emilia)* You tell-tale!

OTHELLO rushes to attack IAGO, but MONTANO stops him.
At the same time, IAGO rushes to attack EMILIA and stabs her with a small knife.
EMILIA looks surprised, but doesn't die immediately.

EMILIA: Iago! Oh! I am slain! Oh cruel life. *(She collapses slowly and balletically to the ground.)* I die.

Photocopiable

EVERYONE stares at EMILIA's body in amazement.

LODOVICO: *(shocked)* He has killed her as well!

GRATIANO: He has slain his wife.

EVERYONE turns and looks accusingly at IAGO.
OTHELLO is becoming distraught.

OTHELLO: Oh my poor Desdemona! I have falsely accused you! I cannot live with my grief and great suffering. I must die.

OTHELLO fiercely pushes MONTANO away, takes out a small knife, stabs himself and dies very dramatically – falling across the body of DESDEMONA.

MONTANO: *(checks OTHELLO for a pulse)* He is dead!

LODOVICO: *(amazed again)* He has killed himself!

There is a dramatic pause while those left alive stand contemplating the mayhem around them.
Suddenly, GRATIANO grabs hold of IAGO.
EVERYONE stands still in silence again.
The DUKE OF VENICE enters. EVERYONE bows to him.

DUKE: Roderigo is lying slain outside. Who has...? *(He stops in amazement at the scene.)* Othello? Desdemona? Emilia? All dead? *(EVERYONE nods.)* How did this happen? I, the Duke of Venice, demand answers!

MONTANO: *(counting them off on his fingers)* Well, Roderigo wounded Cassio, Iago killed Roderigo, Othello killed Desdemona, Iago killed Emilia and Othello killed himself. *(To EVERYONE ELSE)* That's it, isn't it?

EVERYONE ELSE IN UNISON: Yes, that's right.

DUKE: I shall investigate. Gratiano, take Iago away! He shall spend the rest of his days in my least comfortable prison.

GRATIANO: Yes, your honour.

DUKE: Montano, see that Cassio is treated for his wounds. He shall be promoted to take over Othello's position.

MONTANO: Yes, your honour.

DUKE: Lodovico, arrange for Othello and Desdemona to be buried side by side, so that they may be united in death as they never seemed to be in life.

LODOVICO: Yes, your honour.

DUKE: And all of you...

EVERYONE IN UNISON: *(Except IAGO)* Yes, your honour?

DUKE: Get this place cleaned up.

EVERYONE IN UNISON: *(Except IAGO)* Yes, your honour.

They ALL begin to move, then freeze in position as the ANNOUNCER enters.

ANNOUNCER: Well, that was exciting, wasn't it? What a roller-coaster ride of emotions that was! And the moral of our little tale? Well, if there has to be a moral, I suppose that it can be summed up in two words: jealousy kills. So if the green-eyed monster comes knocking on your insecurities – just say no! Thank you.

They ALL begin moving again and continue to tidy up, chatting with each other.
The lights fade to blackout.
The curtains close.

END

PRODUCTION SUPPORT

Three Murders, a Suicide and a Near Miss

AUDITIONS AND CASTING

The easiest way to start the audition process is to read through the play with the children two or three times.

The initial reading should be used simply to familiarize the children with the material. Allocate speeches, reading in sequence around the circle. In the second read-through, let the children volunteer to read specific character parts. In the third, nominate specific children to read certain character parts. During the second and third readings, encourage the children to think about using vocal expression, following the stage directions and picking up their cues quickly. Write yourself notes on how the children perform when reading specific roles. At every read-through, you must give each child a chance to read something.

It is important to make a concerted effort to allow less confident readers a chance to read, encouraging others in the group to show patience and consideration when listening. Plays always help poor readers to develop their language skills, and their enthusiasm for performance often leads to a great deal of work away from rehearsals to make sure that they know their lines. A poor reader does not necessarily make a poor actor.

There are several alternative methods of casting your play, some of which are described below. The process can be as formal or informal as you wish.

FORMAL AUDITIONS

These can be held by selecting specific speeches or scenes from the play and asking the children to learn and recite them, or read them through, in various group combinations. The disadvantages of this method are that it takes an inordinate amount of time to plan and execute, and it makes children very tense and often unable to perform well – especially if their memory skills are not strong.

CHILDREN CHOOSING THEIR OWN ROLES

Another option is to ask the children to write their first and second role choices, confidentially, on pieces of paper. Ask them to try and make sure the spelling is correct, and also to put their full names. Some children will only have one choice of role; some will all go for the same first choice, and there will be some children who 'don't care' what role they are given. Gather all the pieces of paper together and, in a quiet place at another time, sit down and work out who wants what and which role combinations would work.

Try to be as fair as possible, both to the children and to the play. Children are often aware of their 'failings' as actors, and usually accept that others have stronger performance skills; but this doesn't prevent many children from feeling acute disappointment if they fail to secure the role they are desperate for.

When allocating roles after using this method, sit the children in a circle and read from the bottom of the cast list upwards, giving the name of the character first and then the name of the child who has been given that part. Sometimes a little of what is known as 'director speak' (see page 45) may come in handy for convincing upset children that they are more suited to smaller 'character' roles than to a main part. After each part has been given out, allow the children up to 5 minutes to discuss the casting and to accept and compare their roles.

DRAWING NAMES OUT OF A HAT

Another method which is fairer, but more risky for your play, is to ask the children to put their names into a hat and then to draw a name for each character. Children have mixed feelings about this process: there is always a possibility that their name will be drawn for the character they want to play, but they know this is not very likely. Also, less confident children can sometimes end up with large roles which they don't feel happy or comfortable about performing.

CHOOSING ACTORS YOURSELF

The final option is simply to allocate the roles yourself, choosing children who you know are able and confident. However, this can upset other children who are rarely given the opportunity to perform, and removes any sense of the children being involved in the casting process.

After a number of years and arguments, floods of tears and several very unhappy children, I have reached the conclusion that the second method is the fairest and surest option. It gives children a chance to specify which roles they would like to perform, and gives you the opportunity to make a final decision in a considered manner. It always surprises me which parts children choose to go for, and which appear to be the most popular! Sometimes children who appear confident – and who might have otherwise been given a major role – select small parts; likewise, children who appear less confident select major roles.

It is not strictly necessary to cast according to gender. Give females the opportunity to play male

roles, and vice versa. The children will enjoy having the option of selecting a role because of what it is, without being restricted to their own gender.

I feel very strongly that children's enthusiasm for playing their roles will result in an easier rehearsal process, an eagerness to learn lines and a willingness to throw themselves into the roles wholeheartedly. I have been vindicated in this belief over and over again when 'risking' a major part on a child who might not have been given a chance to shine had I used a different method of casting.

Whichever casting method you have used, you should now ask the children to sit in a circle and arrange them according to character or family groups. Read through the play again together, to get the feel of how it sounds with all the roles established.

Finally, tell the children that each person in the cast is as important as the next: without any one character, you don't have a full team and, therefore, a complete play. They won't believe you – they've already spent time counting the number of lines they have to say – but it *is* true, and needs to be expressed.

DIRECTOR SPEAK

Whatever decisions you make about casting, and however fair you try to be, there will be children who are upset when the parts are allocated. Many children feel that they never have the opportunity to show what they can do; some can build up quite a strong resentment against others who always seem to get the main roles; and quieter children can feel a sense of failure at not having pushed themselves forward yet again.

These feelings need to be dealt with as sensitively and as quickly as possible, away from the main group. In these situations, you need to employ what is known

as 'director speak' in an attempt to pacify, boost and reassure the children. This means using a variety of statements aimed to placate, such as:

● *I know you're upset about not getting the part you wanted, but I really needed a good actor for that scene to encourage all the others to perform well.*
● *I understand that you wanted a main part, but you read this part so well that I just had to give it to you.*
● *I appreciate that you're disappointed; but I wanted to give you the chance to try something different this time, to show me what you could do.*
● *I realize you might be a bit disappointed, but this character is very different from your own and will be a challenge for you, which I think you're ready for.*
● *I know that you're unhappy, but can you understand that I have to be fair to everyone and give others a chance to try a bigger part sometimes?*

And others of a similar nature. The children will probably recognize that you are trying to pacify them; but what is important about using 'director speak' is that you are hearing and acknowledging their feelings of unhappiness, and that they have had an opportunity to express these feelings.

Whatever you say is not going to make a lot of difference to some children. In these cases, they need to be given a straightforward choice between playing the part they have been given and not being in the play at all – however cruel that may seem. Most children will choose the former option. Any child opting out of the play should be kept occupied with other tasks, such as painting scenery, prompting or making props and costumes. They will often regret their decision to pull out and, if possible, they should be given the chance to join in again.

The main aspect of the production of a play which is likely to anger and upset children is the part allocation. So if, when using 'director speak' on a previous occasion, you have promised someone a bigger part next time, you must keep your promise! Also, if you have stated that 'everyone needs to be given a chance', then do not under any circumstances allocate the main roles to the same children as were chosen last time.

Remember that all actors have fragile egos, and child actors are no exception. In selecting or auditioning for a role, they are putting themselves firmly in the firing line, exposing their wishes and asking you to praise their abilities, while all the time anticipating that they will be shot down. The worst thing you can do is to negate these feelings and ignore their insecurities. Even as an adult actor, I have felt upset at not being given a part I wanted. Those feelings can be magnified a hundred times for children.

Don't use 'director speak' simply to make life easier for yourself, though it can help to create a positive working environment. I use it all the time, and try to be reasonable, fair and understanding in the way that I use it. In that context, it works.

STRUCTURING REHEARSALS

When faced with directing a play, it is sometimes difficult to know what to tackle first. You have a large group of children awaiting your instructions, a limited amount of access to the school hall, and very little time! Good pre-rehearsal planning and preparation is therefore essential. The following timetable has always worked for me, and might be useful for you.

PREPARATION

Immediately after casting, spend an hour or two resolving practical issues: what sort of stage the play will be performed on; how many entrances and exits the stage will have, and where these will be (plus a consideration of what imaginary setting lies beyond them); where the children will go when they are not on stage; exactly how and where each character enters and exits; what scenery, furniture and props you will have (if any), and where these will be positioned on the stage; whether any characters will enter from other parts of the auditorium and if so, where they will enter from. All of these points need to be clearly defined to your own satisfaction before you start rehearsals.

REHEARSALS 1 TO 3

These should be used to complete what is known as 'blocking' – simply specifying the movements of the children on, off and around the stage. Explain your staging ideas to the cast, marking out the stage area and exits with chairs. Tell the children what furniture and scenery will be on stage, and use chairs or other equipment to represent this as well. Take time to make sure that all of the cast are familiar with the setting, the acting area and their movements before continuing. They'll be desperate to get on with the 'acting', but it is essential that they understand the space they are working in, and know their own moves, before they try to go any further. It is impossible to teach children to act and give them instructions about where to enter and exit at the same time!

REHEARSALS 4 TO 8

Break the play down into small sections and rehearse these individually. Don't try to work through the whole play in a single rehearsal at this point. Start from the beginning and work through a *maximum* of three scenes. Rehearse the same section a number of times,

until you feel that familiarity is beginning to reduce interest; then move on to the next section.

Continue the next rehearsal from where you left off the last time; never repeat the previous section and then move on, or the result will be one or two sections that are absolutely brilliant and a number that are completely under-rehearsed. (I speak from experience!) This will mean that some children are unoccupied for some of the rehearsals. Set them learning their lines in pairs, watching the play and making notes, giving you feedback about how it looks, making props, designing posters and programmes, and so on. Insist that they remain aware of what is going on as they could be called into rehearsal at any time!

Carry on rehearsing the play in small sections until you have completed the whole script. Make notes as you go along of any potential difficulties; any scenes or characters which you feel will need extra rehearsing; and any ideas that you have for scenery, props, costumes or effects.

REHEARSALS 9 TO 11

Use these rehearsals to concentrate on scenes or sections that need extra attention. Try to get through the whole play at least once during each rehearsal period, but don't worry if you fail to do so! Again, never go back over sections: always start the next rehearsal from the point at which you finished the last one. Sections that have not gone well should be repeated afterwards or at a later date, not straight away.

REHEARSALS 12 TO 14

These should be used for complete run-throughs: a technical rehearsal to go over any lights, sound effects, props or music you might be including; and two dress rehearsals complete with costumes and make-up. Spend 10 minutes at the beginning of the final dress rehearsal to work out and practise your 'curtain call', then run through the play completely without stopping.

Final rehearsals are always a nightmare: the children are stressed and excited, you're stressed and beginning to panic, and everyone seems to be snapping at each other! Try to keep the children

occupied at all times. Plan what you want to achieve in the rehearsals, and try to stick to your plan.

I appreciate that this is a rehearsal structure for an 'ideal world', one which doesn't take into account those little things sent to try us: children being absent, falling out, not learning their lines or forgetting everything they learned at the last rehearsal; props and costumes failing to materialize... But those stresses are what give us the sense of achievement when the play finally goes on – and it *does* always go on, despite the horrendous feeling that it will fail. The old saying 'It'll be all right on the night' always applies!

STAGING AND SCENERY

Three Murders, a Suicide and a Near Miss can be very simple to stage. It was first performed on a 'proscenium arch' stage: a square, raised stage that resembles a box, with structured spaces at the side for 'wings' and full curtains (see illustration above). There was no set at all, the stage was completely bare and the children performed against a simple background of black curtains. Any props or furniture used were brought on and removed by the actors. The only drawback of performing on a bare stage is that the children need to work that much harder in their acting to establish settings and create atmospheres.

The ANNOUNCER/NARRATOR was positioned at the very front of the stage, in front of the closed curtains, and returned to that position at the end of the play. You could select any place in your performance arena for NARRATORS to stand – including, perhaps, a separate rostrum at the side of the stage, so that they could watch the play along with the audience.

The majority of the characters in the play simply walked on from the wings at the side of the stage to make their entrances, and exited in the same manner. All the sections of the stage were used to good effect. For example: the small groupings were carefully positioned both upstage and downstage; the actors playing CLOWN and IDIOT tumbled onto and around the stage; the three GUARDS were positioned centre stage, facing the audience at all times; and the growing emotional distance between OTHELLO and

DESDEMONA was highlighted in Scene 5 by gradually moving the actors playing those characters further apart, until they were speaking their lines from opposite sides of the stage.

Furniture was kept to a minimum. The chairs required in Scene 3 (which also served as a 'bed' in Scene 7) were brought on, positioned and removed by the actors. Two chairs placed 'seat to seat' and draped with a piece of material work perfectly adequately as a bed – but it requires a lot of practice for three or four cast members to set it quickly.

Our audience accepted the different settings in the play without the need for elaborate scenery, and this play can work if performed simply against black curtains. The essential consideration, if you are staging it in this way, is *pace*. Keep the entrances and exits swift, blending them as often as possible: when a character is leaving in one direction, a different character can enter from another.

Similarly, work hard to ensure that the scenes do not become too static in their use of space. Remember that actors do not have to restrict their entrances and exits to the stage area alone. You can create interesting effects, including audience diversion, by using other areas of the hall.

This should all provide enough variety to keep the audience interested without your having to resort to creating elaborate scene changes. However, if you want to be more adventurous and use scenery, a number of options are open to you.

If your children are performing on a proscenium arch stage, the solid back wall (known as the cyclorama or cyc) can be decorated with fixed scenery that will be appropriate for most of the scenes in the play, or that presents a general theme. The scenery could be a 'brick wall' pattern, house fronts, shop fronts (to illustrate the town square), or trees and flowers. These elements could be used in any combination to decorate the cyclorama and/or the proscenium arches. Alternatively, you could apply the 'general theme' idea to this play by decorating your stage with images related to jealousy and revenge, such as broken hearts, 'green-eyed monsters', knives dripping with blood, DESDEMONA's handkerchief and

so on. These motifs could be left as a permanent scenery effect throughout the play. Any of these ideas would provide fixed scenery suitable for the majority of the scenes.

Any scenery effects for decorating your stage can be painted onto large sheets of lining paper or fabric, and fixed to the proscenium arches to avoid leaving permanent marks. A similar process would work for the scenery attached to the cyc. if it is also unfeasible to decorate that permanently. Just make sure that whatever you use to attach the scenery holds it on well!

If you are performing the play on a raised rostrum (as in many schools), you could create simple wooden or cardboard screens to act as wings (on either side of the stage) and a back wall. You could decorate these with the 'jealousy' and revenge' motifs, brickwork patterns, house fronts, shop fronts or trees and flowers. Room dividers, or similar, are useful for this. Again, the screens can remain in place throughout the play, acting as a permanent backdrop for all the scenes.

If, however, you would like to change the scenery for each new setting, you will obviously require some form of changeable backdrop. If you have a pulley system at your school, you can use this to hang painted backdrops. However, you are limited to the number of backdrops you can fit on a pulley system, and so this method is not ideal. Other options include:

● Painting scenery onto large sheets of fabric and draping these over a long clothes rail (the type you find in warehouses or large stores). The rail can be swung round on castors to show the other side of any painted cloth, providing an instant scene change.
● Painting scenery onto large wooden or cardboard screens with castors attached, and wheeling these on to provide a moveable backdrop.
● Asking any potential carpenters to make a large wooden frame, approximately 8' × 6'. Attach a large piece of muslin or cotton to it firmly, then stretch the fabric tightly across and around the

edge of the frame. Fix castors to the bottom and paint your scenery onto it. This can then be wheeled on to provide an instant backdrop. Fabric could be attached to both sides of the frame, providing two backdrops. The main problem then is getting the large screens on and off the stage, and storing them when they are not in use!

● Fixing a long, detachable pole across the back of the stage area and attaching several pieces of fabric, with a different scene painted on each one, in a 'flip chart' arrangement. The backdrops can then be flipped over at appropriate points.

● Using the same detachable pole, but drawing the fabric like a curtain across the back of the staging area. This will only provide one scenery change, however.

● If you are performing on a proscenium arch stage and have curtains at the back, these can be closed over any scenery painted on the cyclorama to provide an instant change. It is essential, though, that someone remembers to open them again if you need to return to your original setting.

Whatever you choose, please remember two things:

1. It is no great shame to select fixed scenery as an option. It is much better to spend what limited time and resources you have in creating a wonderfully elaborate setting that remains fixed, than to fail in trying to create a large variety of different scenery effects.

2. If you choose to have moveable scenery, someone has to be responsible for bringing it on and taking it off at the right times, and that you have to find somewhere for it to 'live' when not in use. The same rule applies to any changeable scenery: it has to be changed by someone, who also has to remember to change it back again if required.

If your actors have to bring on and remove any scenery, furniture or props, make sure that everyone is clear about what they are responsible for and rehearse the scene changes as many times as you can. Audiences will forgive most things, but lengthy scene changes always cause them a great deal of irritation!

LIGHTING

Lighting in a play should be used to establish time, enhance setting or create atmosphere. If you are lucky enough to have a professional theatre lighting rig, you can create some wonderful lighting effects. If not, simple lighting can often be sufficient to establish the basics.

Our production of *Three Murders, a Suicide and a Near Miss* was lit very simply with what is known as a 'general wash': the stage was flooded with light. The action in the play appears to take place during the same day and night, reducing the need for elaborate time changes and allowing the lighting to remain fairly constant throughout the play.

If you have the facility to dim or increase your lights, use this to good effect – especially to illustrate the darkening of the evening as IAGO and RODERIGO wait to pounce upon CASSIO, and to create a sinister atmosphere when OTHELLO strangles DESDEMONA. If you do not have the facility to change any of the lights, simply leave them all on for the whole play: this will add to the comedic effect of the piece! An alternative option would be to borrow or hire some free-standing lights, which could be positioned at the side of the stage and used to create atmospheric effects when required.

If you have a professional lighting rig, you could use coloured 'gels' to create some atmospheric lighting effects. These are transparencies which fit over your spotlights to give them a coloured glow. They have to be heat-resistant, and can only be purchased from a theatre lighting specialist. A couple of spotlights with green and blue gels attached, combined with standard (clear white) spots, will give an excellent 'gloomy' setting for the night attack on CASSIO, and could be used again to light the murder of DESDEMONA. Another option, if you have a more sophisticated lighting rig, is to use coloured gels to light the stage briefly each time that Iago enters or leaves – thus representing the darkness of his character. This effect would need to be subtle and well-executed to avoid irritating the audience.

We were fortunate enough to have access to professional spotlights for our production, but still kept the lighting effects extremely simple (as described above). For most of the scenes, the stage was simply flooded with light – not subtle, but effective. Blackouts (extinguishing all lights) were used for scene changes, and in preparation for the 'curtain call'. For a stage with no front curtains, blackouts of this kind can be useful – but make sure that your actors have practised moving around in the dark!

MUSIC AND SOUND EFFECTS

Although we didn't use any music in our production of *Three Murders, a Suicide and a Near Miss*, it could be used effectively to create atmosphere and set the scene. Choose any songs or musical extracts which reflect the themes of 'jealousy' and 'revenge', and select one to use at the beginning and end of the play. This will act as a 'curtain', signalling to the audience when the play is starting and ending. (Before using music in a public performance, check that your school has the relevant broadcast licences.)

Other musical extracts could be included at various points during the play:

● A suitable song could be included to reflect the joy felt by OTHELLO and DESDEMONA when BRABANTINO gives them his blessing in Scene 2.
● RODERIGO sings a sad song as he exits in Scene 2. Our actor sang the line 'I can't live, if living is without you'. This could be turned into a major solo for RODERIGO, placed in between Scenes 2 and 3.
● Slapstick music could underscore the entrance

and antics of CLOWN and IDIOT in Scene 4. Many BBC sound effect CDs contain suitable 'silent movie' music which would work well in this context.
● Sinister music (such as Grieg's 'In the Hall of the Mountain King', or suitable 'silent movie' music) could be used to underscore OTHELLO's meeting with DESDEMONA in Scene 5, emphasizing the impending doom.
● The same music could underscore Scene 7, creating an atmosphere of murder and mayhem.

I don't recommend that any other incidental music is used during the play, though it could be interesting to use music as a character theme by playing the same tune each time a specific character enters. This could work particularly well with IAGO. However, this idea should only really be attempted with one or two characters, and its use should be limited to avoid irritating the audience.

However, if you want to include more music in your production of *Three Murders, a Suicide and a Near Miss*, make your selections carefully. If you have the time, try to search for songs which reflect specific characters' moods, as well as musical extracts which emphasize the general theme.

If you want to reinforce the link to the original Shakespeare text, you could use Elizabethan music throughout. Alternatively, the 'melodrama' idea could be extended by including the play as part of a 'Victorian Music Hall' evening, or by asking a talented pianist to accompany the whole performance (in the way that pianists accompanied the early silent movies).

If you choose to include songs and do not want your 'actors' to sing, other children in the school can

be employed as a chorus. They can be seated around the stage area, singing the songs while those on stage mime appropriate actions.

Also, don't forget to utilize your talented school musicians – both teachers and pupils! The music doesn't have to be tuneful or played from musical scores. Interesting 'musical sound effects' can be created with a variety of unusual or home-made instruments. My big moment (as a teacher) in a school production was providing the 'elephant' sounds on a baritone horn for a performance of *The Jungle Book*!

PROPS

Again, this play is very simple to stage. The only 'props' (an abbreviation of 'properties') which could be included are:

- A large book for the ANNOUNCER/NARRATOR to appear to read from. The script can be concealed inside.
- A flower for RODERIGO to pull the petals from in Scene 1. We used a real flower!
- Chairs for BIANCA, EMILIA and TIFFANIA to sit on in Scene 3.
- 'Pig bladders' on sticks for CLOWN and IDIOT to hit each other with in Scene 4.
- The beautiful lace handkerchief 'found' by IAGO and shown to OTHELLO in Scene 5.
- A placard reading 'Just after midnight' in large letters for Scene 6.
- Swords for CASSIO and RODERIGO to use when fighting in Scene 6.
- A 'bed' for DESDEMONA to lie on in Scene 7.
- A small knife for IAGO to use to kill EMILIA in Scene 7.
- A small knife for OTHELLO to use to kill himself in Scene 7. (He could take it from EMILIA's body!)

Few of these items are actually essential, however. Many of them could be omitted or mimed. The list above consists of all the props that we used (except that we didn't use a placard – we had a child enter, say 'Just after midnight' and then exit again).

We made our 'pig bladders' using pink rubber gloves, blown up and taped firmly to small pieces of wooden doweling. With a little occasional patching and mending, they managed to survive the rehearsals and performance.

We used plastic swords for the fight scene, turning it into a comedy routine with standard, regimented moves which were overemphasized by the actors.

The 'bed' was created by pushing two chairs together and covering them with a piece of beautiful velvet fabric. This is simple and quite effective. If you

have a suitable item of furniture that could be used as a bed, then do use it – but remember that too much furniture on stage is a distraction to your actors and the audience.

Knives (quite rightly) cannot be purchased in toy shops these days. We made some by taking plastic knives, then covering the handles with brown tissue paper and the blades with silver foil. Close up, they looked like plastic knives 'dressed up' – but from a short distance, they looked like lethal daggers!

If your actors react appropriately to any props on stage, then the audience will believe what they see. Also, the distance between stage and audience always helps to create believable illusions – so technical perfection is rarely needed.

The essential point to remember with all props and furniture is: 'If it goes on, it must come off.' If an item makes its way onto the stage, then it must somehow make its way off again! Actors (of all ages) are notoriously bad at remembering this.

COSTUMES

The costumes needed for *Three Murders, a Suicide and a Near Miss* are also very simple. We used a mixture of modern and 'Victorian melodrama' dress, which worked well for the style of the play. If you have the time, resources and skill to create elaborate costumes, then feel free to do so! Your options are: to use modern dress for every character; to dress your actors in Elizabethan costumes (linking to the Shakespeare theme); or to select costumes which reflect the concept of a Victorian melodrama. If time, resources and skill are lacking, you could use the following ideas, which worked perfectly well for our production:

Announcer/Narrator was dressed in his own smart clothes – black trousers, white shirt, black bow tie, smart shoes and bright-coloured waistcoat. For any narrators, I feel that it is better to have a colour scheme: all in black and white, all in red and black, or similar. This is so that they are dressed in some form of recognizable 'costume' – and, more importantly, that they feel they are. Narrators need the thrill of 'dressing up' too! Alternatively, you could always dress your narrators in a costume that links to the play's themes or storyline.

Iago was dressed all in black: trousers, a shirt, shoes and a flowing cape.

Roderigo was dressed in bright colours: green satin trousers, a colourful flowery shirt and coloured pumps. He also had a coloured silk handkerchief in his shirt pocket.

Three Murders, a Suicide and a Near Miss

Cassio was dressed in smart clothes: brown trousers, a cream shirt, a brown leather waistcoat and smart boots (shoes will suffice). We cut the collar off the shirt and gave him a thick brown leather belt to carry his sword in.

Brabantino was supposed to have been roused from his bed, so we dressed him in a long dressing gown, pyjamas and big fluffy slippers.

Othello was dressed in smart black trousers, a smart white shirt with the collar removed, smart shoes, an elaborate waistcoat and a brown velvet jacket.

Desdemona wore a beautiful, full-length blue taffeta dress, with a matching shawl. She wore gold slippers – but ballet shoes or any other 'dressy' shoes would work just as well. The shawl could be left out, as it does tend to fall off regularly!

The Duke of Venice was dressed in smart black trousers, black boots (Wellington boots would work well), a smart white shirt, a silk cravat and a smart black dinner jacket. We found a black tailcoat jacket in a charity shop that looked wonderful.

Bianca, Emilia and **Tiffania** were dressed in their own modern clothes. They wore very short dresses (or skirts combined with tight-fitting tops) and smart shoes (not trainers) with heels; they had bare legs. They looked every inch the 'silly young things' they were! You might like to give them tiny PVC rucksacks as well.

Montano, Lodovico and **Gratiano** were dressed in glittery tunic tops, coloured tights and black pumps. We made silver buckles from card and silver foil, and attached these to the pumps with pieces of black elastic. The tops were purchased from a local charity shop. If you can't find glittery tunic tops, you could spray other tops with glitter.

Clown and **Idiot** were dressed in 'clown' outfits: bright-coloured shirts and colourful baggy trousers held up with coloured braces. They had bare feet and wore coloured neckerchiefs (made simply from pieces of fabric) around their necks.

Messengers 1, 2 and **3** were dressed as postmen. They wore blue trousers, blue jackets, white shirts (blue shirts would be better, if possible), smart white shoes and blue ties; they carried large bags over their shoulders. A kind parent sewed red piping down the outside edge of the trousers and along the shoulders of the jackets.

Guards 1, 2 and 3 were dressed as nightclub bouncers! They wore smart black trousers, white shirts, black bow ties, smart black shoes (pumps will do), black sunglasses and black jackets (school blazers with the badges removed will do if you can't find any other suitable jackets).

MAKE-UP

All make-up depends on the type of lighting used in your performance arena. If you are working under professional stage lights, then more make-up needs to be applied, since these lights remove colour and contour from the face. However, if you are working under school lights or strip lights, be careful just to define features and express the characters. Water-based make-up is best for whole face or body coverage; grease-based make-up is best for eyes, cheeks and lips. Both types of make-up can be purchased from any good theatrical costumier's, and many specialist companies provide a large variety of water-based face paints and theatre make-up. Practise applying make-up before the performances!

The make-up for *Three Murders, a Suicide and a Near Miss* is extremely simple, and very little of it is needed. The following were used in our production:

Announcer/Narrator was given a light base of foundation, light lipstick and blue eye shadow. We also gave him a large, curly moustache (drawn on with black eyeliner pencil) to emphasize his role as anouncer of a 'Victorian melodrama'. Always try to prevent narrators from applying too much make-up, as it is not necessary. It is more important that they look clean, tidy and smart.

Male characters were given a light base of foundation, blue eye shadow, a slight touch of pale red blusher and pale red lips. We drew a fantastic curly moustache on IAGO, again using a black eyeliner pencil. One or two of the 'important officials' could also be given slightly red noses (using a grease stick) to indicate 'good living'.

Female characters were given a light base, lots of blue eye shadow, a darker red blusher and bright red or pink lipstick. Take care not to give DESDEMONA too much make-up, however: she needs to look beautiful rather than comical.

Clown and **Idiot** were not given full clown make-up. We gave them an ordinary base of foundation, bright-coloured eyeshadow, coloured lips and circles of colour on their cheeks, and coloured the ends of their noses with red grease paint.

Guards could be given facial scars to make them look 'hard' if you wish. Draw these on with a black eyeliner pencil, then add dark purple grease paint applied with a cocktail stick.

Messengers and/or **Brabantino** could be given facial stubble. Take a small blusher brush, stipple brush or stipple sponge, cover it with black grease paint and dab carefully over the chin, part of the neck area and cheeks. Ask the children to suck their lips in to ensure complete coverage. I prefer to use a blusher brush, end on, as it gives a better effect.

If you want to 'age' your children, use a red-toned grease stick and a cocktail stick. Ask the children to screw up their faces and apply the grease paint to the wrinkles with the cocktail stick. Think carefully about where wrinkles form on the face as you age, and draw them accordingly. However, be careful not to draw in too many lines, or the poor child will end up with a face like a road map!

If you want to give IAGO a real moustache to twirl, fake hair can be purchased for this purpose. It comes in small plaits or strips, and needs teasing into shape. You then fix it to the face using spirit gum, which should hold it on firmly throughout the performance.

Any base or foundation should be applied all over the face and neck area, including the ears and the back of the neck. A small amount of make-up must also be used to cover any other areas of bare flesh, such as arms and hands. For large expanses of skin, water-based make-up is quickest and most effective. It is important to cover all 'bare flesh' areas, especially if working under professional theatre lighting, as the lights will show very clearly the difference between made-up and non-made-up flesh.

Face paints (water-based cake make-up) need to be applied with a sponge that is barely damp and fully covered with make-up. If you have too much water on your sponge, the make-up will streak and application will be patchy. If you decide to use grease sticks to create a base or foundation, select a brick red and a colour slightly paler than the child's skin. Apply the pale colour all over the face, blending well with your fingers, then dot the red on the forehead, cheeks, chin and nose and blend this in thoroughly and carefully. The face should now have a good base on which you can apply other colours. If not, keep adding more of either colour and blending thoroughly until you are happy with the result. Use the same technique for all other areas of bare skin.

'Set' any grease make-up with a light dusting of loose powder to keep it in place under the hot stage lights. Take care when applying blusher using a grease stick as a little goes a very long way! Grease sticks for eye shadow come in a variety of colours (not just blue), and any of these can be used to make up your characters. However, green eye shadow is *never* worn in the theatre – you have been warned!

Try to avoid using ordinary make-up for the stage: it is not suitable and rarely withstands the heat, often fading within a few minutes of being applied. Theatre make-up is specifically designed for the stage, and it is worth spending £20 or £30 on purchasing a good selection of proper theatrical make-up.

Other items which would be useful for your make-up box include: hair gel, talcum powder (for whitening hair), fake blood (mix glycerine with red food colouring), a stipple brush (or small blusher brush) and black grease stick for creating facial stubble, fake hair and spirit gum for applying it, cocktail sticks for creating age lines, teeth blackout liquid, coloured hair spray, glitter gels, and a variety of coloured grease sticks.

LEARNING LINES

Children never fail to amaze me with their capacity for learning and retaining lines. However, everyone needs support in learning lines at some time. Methods that can help include the following:

REPETITION

This requires frequent and regular reading of the script. Go over the children's lines again and again, and they will learn them by rote. This method means that children often learn everyone else's lines as well – which is not a problem unless they start prompting while on stage.

FROM CUES

Read the line immediately before a child's. Let the child read his or her line out loud. Read the 'cue line' again, but this time cover up the child's line on the script. This way, the children are learning the important cues as well as their own lines.

ON PAPER

Write each child's cue lines and own lines on a separate piece of paper, to prevent the children being daunted by a large script. Use this method for children to learn one scene or short section at a time. They can carry the pieces of paper around with them, and will memorize the lines quite quickly through absorbing these short extracts.

ON TAPE

Help the children to read through the script two or three times. Record each child's cue lines on tape, leaving a long pause after each one for the child to interject his or her own lines. Work through this with each child initially, using the script as an accompanying visual aid; then let the children try it alone. Gradually remove their dependence on using the script, until they can say their lines in the recorded pauses without hesitating. Alternatively, you could record both the cue lines and the child's own lines, then leave a gap for the child to repeat his or her own lines.

VERBAL SUPPORT

Some children find it easier to learn lines through hearing them spoken and simply repeating them. However, this can take up an awful lot of your rehearsal time!

In addition, enlist the support of family members to help the children with their lines. Encourage children to 'test' each other, and try to create an atmosphere of support. Don't be too worried if the children paraphrase their lines, as long as important aspects are not omitted.

Use what literacy time you can spare to read through the script a number of times as a whole group. Take a balanced approach: emphasize that the children need to remember what they will say, but don't frighten them so much that they forget everything!

Children should, however, be aware of the fact that

they will not be able to take their scripts (or pieces of paper) onto the stage with them. This should be made clear as early in the rehearsal process as possible, to make sure that they all understand.

The most secure approach is to make sure that the children know (and if possible, learn) the whole script. This builds knowledge of what should happen in each scene, and means that the children can say or improvise another character's lines if something goes wrong.

If you have the time, include one or two 'line learn rehearsals' in your schedule. Sit with the children in a circle, positioning them in character order, then instruct them to recite the whole play with their scripts placed face down on the floor in front of them. This can help the person prompting to appreciate his or her job as well. It also makes you aware of which children need more help with learning their lines.

Prompters should only give the first word of a sentence, then supply more words if the actor is still struggling. Make sure that only one person is responsible for prompting, and give him or her every possible opportunity to practise.

It is also a good idea to tell the children a specific day by which they must have learned all of their lines. Tell them which rehearsal this will be – and stick to it! At that rehearsal, don't allow any children to go on with their scripts in hand. It will be a slow, painful process and the prompter will work overtime, but it is a necessary evil! Scripts are like security blankets: all actors panic when they are taken away. Try to intersperse 'no scripts' rehearsals with additional 'line learn' rehearsals to boost their confidence.

A final note: NEVER allow children to write lines on themselves. A girl of ten recently came to the dress rehearsal with her four lines written all over the palm of one hand. Even though they would have faded by the time the play went on that day, I very cruelly made her wash them off! Although she stumbled a little, she remembered her lines and felt a greater sense of achievement than she would have if she had simply read them. It is *not* acceptable for actors to have lines written down anywhere on their person, or on pieces of paper on the stage. Apart from affecting the quality of the performance, it is a risk: what happens if you lose your place while reading, the lines fade from your skin, or someone moves your piece of paper?

CALMING NERVES AND CHANNELLING ENERGY

Those children who become stressed and nervous about performing must be allowed to feel that they have a 'get-out clause'. If possible, have another child in mind who can take over their lines, and let them know that they don't have to perform if they *really* don't want to. I say this on a regular basis to the young children I direct; and however terrified they may become, they always end up performing. I think this is because they know that taking part in the play is *their* choice, and that they can pull out at any time if they really want to.

Give the more 'energetic' (a euphemism for 'disruptive'!) children specific tasks to perform. I often involve these children in helping others to learn lines, in making props and even in applying make-up during rehearsals. Having a sense of responsibility about an important job will usually calm over-excited children. However, there is always the option of threatening to remove them from the play – and meaning it – if they don't calm down.

The trick is to keep all the children occupied throughout the build-up to the performance. This prevents them from having time to be worried, and uses up spare energy. Use your rehearsal planning time to set up two or three production-related tasks that can be done while the rehearsals are in progress. Alternatively, bring drawing paper and crayons to rehearsals and ask children to draw the stage and set. I have also used word puzzles and colouring books, and asked children to write and decorate invitations for their families to come and see the play. All obvious strategies, but they work!

CURTAIN CALLS

I have seen some terrible curtain calls which have completely spoiled an otherwise good performance. Bear in mind that this is the last memory your audience will have of the play, and that any sloppiness at this point will override the professionalism that may have gone before.

I'm not in favour of the pantomime-style 'walkdown' curtain call where the actors come on to take their bows one by one to different audience responses. In fact, I'm completely against them. It must feel awful to act your heart out and then come on to a lukewarm reception when your co-actor has just received a rousing, foot-stamping cheer.

I prefer to structure my curtain calls as follows:

- Line up all the children on stage in several rows according to height, with the tallest ones at the back. Space them out so they can all be seen.
- Tell the children to look around and notice who they are standing next to, in front of and behind.
- Tell all the children to stand upright, with their feet together and their hands resting lightly on the front of their thighs.
- Now nominate one child in the centre of the front row to start the bow. Tell all the other children to watch this child carefully, without making their observations noticeable.
- When the nominated child on the front row bows slowly, everyone must bow. Bowing should be done from the waist, with the hands sliding down to the knees and the eyes directed at the floor. Make sure that everyone moves at the same, slow pace: bowing too quickly can give the appearance of a group of nodding ducks!
- Tell the children to hold the bowing position for a slow count of two; then everyone should straighten up again.
- Repeat, with everyone following the front row leader.

That is all that's required!

Finally, make sure that the children maintain the same level of professionalism when leaving the stage. Don't allow them to scream, shout, wave to their parents or whatever. A smooth, professional ending can really round off a lovely performance.

LITERACY SUPPORT

The following are some brief suggestions for literacy activities that could follow on from reading and performing the playscript.

STORY

Ask the children to retell the story. This could be done in a number of ways:
- Groups retelling different sections in sequence, with the class as audience.
- Storyboarding the main events, with or without captions, in small groups or as a whole class.
- Recording the main incidents in single sentences with accompanying pictures to create a 'wall story'.

Ask the children to devise an alternative ending for the play, then improvise and record it (in writing or on cassette).

CHARACTERS

The children could perform the play using simple puppets, paying particular attention to the voices of different characters and narrators.

They could write a description of their favourite character, choosing suitable adjectives to describe characteristics and physical appearance.

They could write the play as a story told from OTHELLO's point of view.

THEME

Ask the children what they think the main theme of the play is (for example, 'jealousy and revenge'). They can work in small groups to improvise and then write a short play about the same theme. The plays can be performed to the class.

The children could write a short story that describes a situation where someone feels jealous.

WORKING WITH THE PLAYSCRIPT

Explore the layout conventions of playscripts, using a short section of the text. Look together at how stage directions are written, how the scenes are structured and so on. Can the children explain these conventions?

Ask the children to devise a 'Glossary of Terms' to accompany the play, defining difficult or obscure words and phrases.

Ask the children to look at the bracketed stage directions in the playscript which are used for character expression. Can they find at least three adverbs which have been formed using the suffix '-ly' (such as 'sadly' or 'nervously')? Ask them to use these adverbs as a basis for writing a short story.

PERFORMANCE-RELATED TASKS

Ask the children to write and design a programme for the play that gives the audience all the relevant information.

The children could design and draw the set for Scenes 4 and 6, writing down arguments to support their choice of design.

The children could design and draw a costume for their least favourite character, then explain how this costume expresses the character's personality, give reasons for their choice of materials, and say how their costume design reflects the place and time in which the play is set.